SHATTERED TRUTHS

THE PAST HIDES A SECRET

DAVID JOWSEY

Sigel Press

Sigel Press
51A Victoria Road
Cambridge CB4 3BW England

4403 Belmont Court
Medina, Ohio 44256 USA

Visit us on the World Wide Web at **www.sigelpress.com**

First published 2009

Cover image by David Jowsey
Cover and internal design by Harp Mando

ISBN 10: 1-905941-02-1
ISBN 13: 978-1-905941-02-5

A catalogue record for this book is available from the British Library.
Typeset in: 10/13pt Janson Text

In North America: Printed and bound in the United States
In Europe: Printed and bound in the UK by Henry Ling Limited,
Dorchester
10 9 8 7 6 5 4 3 2 1

The publisher's policy is to use paper manufactured from sustainable
forests.

ACKNOWLEDGEMENTS

Writing a sequel is never an easy task, as so many authors have said, and sitting down to write a sequel to my debut novel has proved every one of them right. But in doing so I have had the help and support of many people to whom I am indebted:

To the team at Sigel Press: my publisher, Thomas Sigel, for his unwavering support and enthusiasm; to my editor, Andrew Hogbin for his useful input; to Harp Mando for typesetting and the wonderful cover and back cover design.

To Barbara Demby and Dory Stewart: thank you for your comments and suggestions during the draft stages of the manuscript.

To my wife Dianne: thank you for your support, encouragement and critical eye, and for putting up with me writing at odd hours of the day and night.

To Ellie-May (my number one!): thank you for your excitement and interest in my projects, and to Leanne, Stuart and Craig, thank you for your support and interest. I would also like to express gratitude to my wonderful parents, extended family, friends, colleagues and pupils, all of whom have encouraged me throughout.

To Mars Planetary Scientist Dr. Michael A. Mischna: thank you for detailed advice about the composition of the Martian surface and atmosphere and for correcting my scientific inaccuracies throughout.

To John Williams, Howard Shore, Jon Anderson and Vangelis: Your music has been the background to my writing; and to

Arthur C. Clarke, Carl Sagan and Stephen Baxter: these are the men whose vision and zest have provided so much inspiration and direction. Thank you.

Finally, and without whom none of this would have any meaning: to the readers who enjoyed *Dragons in the Sky* and have repeatedly asked about a sequel. I hope this book has met your expectations, and I look forward to completing the trilogy.

For further information visit:

www.davidjowsey.com, www.sigelpress.com

or email me at:

shatteredtruths@hotmail.co.uk

Thank you all.

David Jowsey
June 2009

ABOUT THE AUTHOR

David Jowsey was born and raised in Middlesbrough, and continues to live and work in the area. He trained as a primary school teacher at Bretton Hall College, Wakefield, where he studied Visual Arts, graduating in 1988. He started his teaching career at Tedder Junior School and is currently a teacher at Ravensworth Junior School in Normanby.

In his spare time David enjoys art and music. He was a founding member of the Band of '78 where he became a competent trombone player, and now shares his skills and experience teaching local children within the band.

David's knowledge of the local area, along with his art skills, have enabled him to illustrate *Dragons in the Sky* and *Shattered Truths*.

AUTHOR'S NOTE

During the writing of *Shattered Truths* I was guided on scientific issues by Mars Planetary Scientist, Dr. Michael A. Mischna. I am indebted to him for all his time and help.

I wish to make it clear that the impact of Phobos and the resulting global catastrophe, the visibility of Mount Olympus Mons from the Martian surface, (in reality the slope of its volcanic shield would be impossible to see from anywhere on the surface), and the rapid thickening of the Martian atmosphere are the result of artistic licence on the part of the author, and are my responsibility entirely.

Crop circles, the Phobos 1 photographs and the MAJESTIC 12 are well documented conspiracy theories, but whether their stories hold any truth remains to be seen. For the purposes of *Shattered Truths* they have proved to be a useful vehicle for storytelling, and where I have resorted to exaggeration, sensationalism or scientific inaccuracy, I hope I will be forgiven.

For Kel and for Pete.
Two great friends, sadly missed.

PROLOGUE

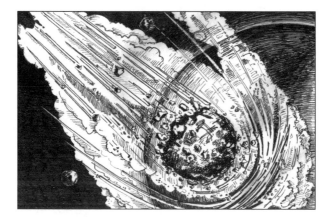

4.3 billion years ago

Through the penetrating cold of deep space, the asteroid fell towards a single yellow star. It passed the outer gas giants; their rings of ice and dust glittered like diamonds in the night, their cloud tops stained red and ochre, but the asteroid soon left them behind and continued onwards to the inner planets.

Falling ever faster, the asteroid hurtled across the orbit of a frozen world and dragged the planet into the warming rays of its sun. At first the planet's orbit was unstable, and the world threatened to break itself apart, but gradually its orbit settled and the surface began to thaw.

It was a world with great potential.

Passing close behind the burning star, the asteroid picked up speed. Its surface seethed and bubbled, its core cracking under the searing heat, until finally it was hurled back into the icy cold of deep space.

It would drift silently for millions of years, but it would fall sunward once more.

Next time its effect would be devastating.

DAVID JOWSEY

CHAPTER 1

A warm breeze caressed him, the sun's rays pleasant against his skin, but as he soaked up the moment something sharp struck the back of his neck.

He reached up and found his hand streaked with red; he wiped again with his other hand and found it the same, but it was not blood.

The breeze stirred and a faint odour filled his senses. He raised his fingers cautiously to his nose and inhaled, the redness gritty against his skin, and wrinkled his nose in disgust.

Sulphur.

Without warning, his back felt cold to the point of discomfort. Almost icy. He shivered, his skin crawling with the sudden temperature drop as more pin-pricks - painfully sharp stings accentuated by the sudden cold - racked his body.

He picked up a fistful of sand and watched as its coarse grains cascaded through his fingers like liquid from a jug, shivering as the red snow drifted and billowed in the strengthening wind. Whipped into swirling clouds, the sky was filled with dust, and as he watched, all traces of summer blue vanished.

When the full force of the wind struck it was like a battering ram. He fumbled, grasping at handfuls of red sand and buried grass to steady himself, and managed to keep from falling backwards.

This isn't real, he thought. *This can't be happening.*

He scrambled to his feet and forced himself toward the bridge he had crossed little more than an hour before. Blinded by stinging dust, and with his breathing impeded by painful coughs and splutters, he steeled himself against the biting cold.

Step by step he struggled on, leaning into the howling wind and teetering unsteadily as the gusts increased. Finally, he was forced down, and could rise no more.

The dust blew in swirling drifts around his shuddering form. It blanketed itself over his body and he struggled to breathe, until, with a final gasp at life, he surrendered and lay still.

The open cavity of a mouth, which had once smiled so happily at the beauty of a summer's day, now lay dry and unmoving. Dust swirled inside, filled the open space and clogged the airway to leave nothing exposed but a single area of flesh.

It was the only evidence that Tom Richards had ever existed.

CHAPTER 2

Tom landed hard on the cold metal floor. He leaned forwards and retched heavily while his hands clawed at his clogged throat.

A metallic *clang* rang out in the darkness as the hatch opened. A figure poked its head into the room and Tom felt himself lifted.

'Whoa - gotcha!' Tiny reached out with a free hand and flicked on the light. It glowed dimly at first before steadily increasing in brightness.

Tom coughed again and then raised a hand. 'Sorry. Bad dream.' He rubbed his face and forced a smile. His voice was thick. 'I'm okay. Thanks.'

'You sure?'

'Yeah.' He nodded, trying to convince Tiny, and then coughed again. Tiny drew a cup of water from the dispenser on the wall and offered it. Tom gulped it heartily and handed the cup back. 'More,' he croaked.

The big Australian watched with an intense scrutiny as Tom drained the second cupful. He knew Tom Richards well and sensed immediately that something was wrong – that his friend had experienced more than just a nightmare. His perception was borne of a close friendship forged during their early days at NASA. Although they hailed from very different backgrounds, their differences were the glue that had cemented their friendship.

Now Tiny watched his friend with concern, but decided not to push. It hadn't been the first time over the past few weeks he'd heard his friend cry out during the night. He also knew if Tom wanted to share his problems, he would open up in his own time.

Tiny squatted on the floor and waited. Tom looked troubled, but finally ventured back into the memory of his dream. 'I dreamt I was choking in sand,' he said. 'I could feel it filling my nose and throat. I must have fallen when I sat up to cough.' He looked over at Tiny. 'Pretty stupid, huh?'

'Nah. We've all had 'em at some time or another.' He put his hand on Tom's shoulder and squeezed. 'Anyway, if you're sure you're okay then I'm going back to bed.' Tiny stood up, his bulk seeming to fill Tom's sleeping compartment. He hadn't been nicknamed 'Tiny' for nothing.

'Thanks.' Tom smiled weakly.

'No problem.' Tiny flicked a salute and opened the hatch. Tom let out a big sigh as it *clanged* shut, then coughed again as he rubbed sub-consciously at his throat. 'That was too real,' he mumbled. 'Too real for comfort.' He scrubbed his hand over three days' worth of stubble and yawned, tired but not ready to try to sleep again.

He plucked his sleeping bag from the floor and, rolling it into a ball, sat with it on his lap. He pondered the meaning of his dream before throwing the bag onto his bunk and reaching for the shutter control. The motor whined softly and the window slats parted to reveal an ochre light. It flooded his sleeping compartment and Tom stooped to look out, his forehead pressed against the cold plastic of the window.

Rocky desolation stretched away to the horizon, the low hills to his right and rocky plateau to his left broken only by the tubular structures of *Foothold* station. They shimmered with the softly reflected light of the Martian dawn.

Tom sighed. He felt as though the planet had called him here, and he longed to understand why.

CHAPTER 3

Martian sunlight cut across the rim of the rock-strewn ravine, mottled shadows stretching outwards from its base. Commander Jack Riordan stood within the shadows, his thick-soled boots dusted red by the surface of the planet. His treads left heavy imprints in the dust and he pondered how soon they would last. *Dust storms will soon obliterate them,* he thought. *They'll be gone in no time.* A slight breeze disturbed the dust and his boot prints quickly lost their clarity. He smiled. *And so it begins.*

How different this planet was from the Moon, where footprints would last for eternity.

Jack closed his eyes and allowed his thoughts to drift. Fourteen years ago he had stood much as he was now, staring across the deep craters of the Moon towards the low foothills, its surface scarred with four and a half billion years' worth of meteorite impacts. It boiled by day and froze by night, cracking rocks and crumbling mountains, but with no wind or rain to disturb the footprints he had left behind, they would remain forever.

But Mars was not the Moon; this world was very different.

Jack Riordan had worked hard to attain the position of *Foothold* Mission Commander, and his presence on the Martian surface made him the most experienced astronaut in history. With three tours aboard the International Space Station and two more to *Clarke* Base on the moon, Jack Riordan had logged more space hours, and had spent more time away from Earth than any other astronaut. He had been the logical choice for Commander, and he had been ready.

Jack peered into the ravine below. An Exploration Vehicle stood about two hundred metres away, two white suited figures clustered around it as they set up a collection of scientific instruments. The crew had brought two EVs with them from

Earth, and the vehicles had allowed the *Foothold* crew to travel further than the Apollo astronauts had ever dreamt possible. Each vehicle provided a pressurised environment where the crew could live for up to a month while away from their home base. They could even sustain a crew of three for up to six weeks if necessary.

A thin veil of dust reduced his visibility for a few seconds as the wind gusted, but it quickly passed. He spoke into his mike. 'Time.'

His computer projected a green digital display onto the inside of his visor. He grunted at the numbers and flicked on his radio, picking up a burst of static from the sun high overhead. 'This is Riordan. I'm done here. I'm coming back, but I have some great shots of you guys.' He smiled at the two ant-like figures below him. 'I can't believe how small you look.'

A reply followed on the heels of a brief crackle of static. 'Roger that.'

Jack looked up at the sky, the sun nothing more than a distant circle of light. *She's giving us some trouble today*, he thought. *Solar radiation must be climbing.* He checked his dosimeter and found his radiation readings slightly raised, but nothing worth cutting the mission short.

An accented voice cut in. 'I have something of interest here, Commander.'

Jack's interest was piqued. 'What is it?'

More static. 'I found it at the base of the ravine. You'd better see it for yourself - it's unusual.' When Frank Louville was excited, his French accent could become almost too thick to understand.

'Okay. I'll be there in a few minutes. Pack it for return. Riordan out.' Jack leant forward, propelled himself into momentum in the low gravity, and within a few seconds was bounding downhill through the glory of the early morning sun.

He smiled. Mars was a great place to be.

CHAPTER 4

The wheels of EV-1 kicked up large fountains of dust as the vehicle sped across the desert landscape. Two members of her three-man crew sat around the briefing table on the mid-deck, coffee cups before them. The contents were almost sacred after six hours of drinking recycled water inside a suit that was more uncomfortable than its designer could ever have imagined.

With a *hiss* the pressurised hatch opened and Irina Panova stepped through, her white jump suit and short hair typical of all three members of Team One. She stepped over to the galley, drew a cup of steaming coffee from the dispenser, and settled her slim frame into an empty seat.

'Oh, that tastes good,' she croaked, her Russian accent parched to huskiness by the air recyclers in her suit. Irina sat back and closed her eyes for a moment, her features enhanced by the reddish light streaming in through the viewport.

Irina was petite, but typically Russian with dark eyes and a strong jaw line accentuating her beauty, while her short dark hair capped her head with loose curls. She was the member of the crew the media had seized upon most of all in the run up to launch. They had labelled her the 'Martian Queen', but Irina had refused to take their bait - she had a sharp wit and had rounded quickly, responding that Mars was too far to travel and still look good.

Frank laughed and raised his mug. 'That's just what we said.' He glanced at Jack, excitement making his eyes dance, and took a swig. Its strong flavour was satisfying against the back of his throat, and he swallowed it eagerly.

Frank Louville was *Foothold's* communications and electrical genius. He had enroled for NASA before the excitement of the moon missions in the early 2020s, and had fought hard to land a position on the crew. Nobody had been surprised when his involvement had been announced; it was as if he had always been destined to fly the mission.

After another deep swig, Frank set his mug down on the table and sat back with an excited smile. His grin made his eyes light up, and Irina smiled back. She had been drawn to Frank since the day they had first been introduced, but his olive skin and broad smile had gained him untold female admirers back home too.

Jack broke the moment by tapping at a control on the briefing table. A detailed map of the planet's northern hemisphere appeared. It settled on the outer fringes of the Valles Marineris, a four thousand kilometres long system of canyons which stretched along the Martian equator like a great scar. Jack tapped again and a series of icons began flashing.

'Right, so this is our route so far. We've covered nearly two hundred and seventy kilometres in the past week, visiting two sites every day. Our next stop is just under nine hours from now, and if all goes according to plan the EV should have us there by dawn.'

Despite his excitement Frank stifled a yawn. 'Good. That last surface walk really took it out of me.' He glanced at Irina and she nodded in agreement, but his eyes told her he was far from ready to hit his bunk.

Jack continued. 'So, observations from today. Frank, you said you had something of interest?'

Frank tapped at a small keypad. The map vanished and images flickered into life. 'These are the 3D shots I took of the sample just before we finished our EVA.' The image hovered centimetres above the table, rotating slowly to show a fist-sized rock – a totally unexpected deep purple. They had studied thousands of rocks over the past eight months, but this sample was different. 'Scans picked up the usual chemical traces we'd expect, but there are a multitude of chemical compounds here that the scanners can't decipher.'

Jack frowned. 'So what is it, a deep space meteorite?

'I thought so at first, but then I found this.' Frank tapped at his panel and the image presented a different view. He zoomed in on markings across one small section of the rock. 'I'm not sure what these are. What do you think?'

The markings were badly eroded and barely visible. Jack leaned forward, Irina's head almost touching his as they peered closely. Their eyes were wide in disbelief, and Jack let out a low whistle.

Were these markings an accident of nature, or was this haphazard collection of grooves and indentations something else entirely?

CHAPTER 5

Tom passed the probe to Tiny, stepped back and took a moment to rest. Sweat beaded against his forehead and his visor had already misted over despite the air conditioners whirring inside his suit.

Rather than use the radio Tiny touched his helmet against Tom's. His voice vibrated through the metal. 'How're you doing?'

Tom sipped at his drinking tube and smiled. 'Fine, why?'

'Just checking, mate; thought that bump the other night might have knocked some sense into your thick skull.' Tiny laughed and stepped back, the silence sudden as the metal – to – metal contact was broken. Through his visor Tom could see his friend laughing hysterically. Tom mouthed something in return and Tiny roared again.

'Hey, what's going on? Are you two still at it?' In all the time the crew had been together, Naina Desai had never fully grasped their sense of humour, but it was infectious nevertheless. She watched them, her own reflection distorted by the curve of their visors, and shook her head. 'What's the big joke?'

Tom glanced at his friend, the big man barely managing to hold himself under control, and saw tears glisten as they rolled down his cheeks. The sight made him snigger, and within seconds both men had dissolved into guffaws of uncontrollable laughter. Tiny leaned on Tom's shoulder for support.

Naina shook her head in dismay at the childish behaviour. *What am I going to do with these two?* She shook her head again in disbelief, a broad grin spreading across her face.

Tiny pulled himself back from the absurdity of the moment and slapped Tom on the back as he stood. 'Aw, mate, you really crack me up.' He tried his best to avoid eye contact, knowing the slightest glance would be enough to send him off again, and with a few deep breaths to compose himself, stepped away.

Tiny turned towards Naina, an apology on his lips as he fought to control his voice. It wavered as he spoke, laughter threatening to erupt once again, but faltered as he saw Naina's HardSuit shaking.

'Naina? Are you okay?' He grabbed her by the shoulders and spun her into the light so he could peer through her visor.

Naina's face creased into lines, her eyes squeezed tight shut and her mouth wide open as tears streamed down her cheeks.

She was in fits of laughter.

*   *   *

The merriment of the afternoon had long since passed and EV-2 trundled across the Martian surface when Tom's earpiece crackled to life. It was Tiny.

'Hey, man. You about done down there? Riordan needs to talk to us.'

'Yeah.' He finished wiping the inside of his helmet with an antiseptic wipe and balled it in his fist. 'I'll be with you in five.'

'Okay. Make it snappy, huh? He sounds excited over something.'

'Will do. Five minutes tops.' He stuffed the wipe into a small waste container and connected his HardSuit batteries to a charger, then moved towards the hatch. It took a lot to get the Commander excited; he was a very by-the-book man, but if he wanted the whole crew online together he must have a good reason.

Tom took a final glance at his suit, checked the charging lights were all in the green, and stepped onto the mid-deck.

Jack was speaking excitedly. 'It's a bit of a mystery. It has compounds we don't recognise, and there's something else: it has some kind of an inscription, or at least that's what it appears to be.'

'An inscription?' Tom shushed the voices beside him as they

erupted into excited conversation. Their voices drowned the commander's words and Tom struggled to listen. He waved at Tiny and Naina to quieten down again.

'We don't know. It looks as though it could be part of something larger, but there's also a good chance it may turn out to be natural; unusual fracture marks or some rock pattern we haven't encountered before. Just because it's new to us doesn't mean it hasn't been here all along. It may simply be something unique to this world.'

Tiny sat forward. 'So we take it you're going back to *Foothold* early?'

'Roger that. We need *Foothold's* computers for a detailed analysis, but you carry on as planned and we'll see you tomorrow evening. Hopefully by then we'll have a better idea of what we've found.'

Tom glanced out of the window at the deep expanse of the Valles Marineris. It stretched away into the haze. 'We're about to go into one of the narrower river beds,' said Tom, 'so there's a possibility we may be out of contact for a few hours. We'll radio in as soon as conditions allow.'

'Okay. We'll have the coffee waiting. Riordan out.'

Tom felt an expectant rush of excitement as the channel went dead. He couldn't wait to get onto the surface again, but looked into the tired eyes of his crew mates and saw fatigue lingering there.

'Come on,' he said quietly, 'let's get some sleep. I think we need it.'

CHAPTER 6

As Tom faced the rising sun, he stepped once again onto the cold and inhospitable surface of Mars. Small rock falls skittered down the hillside as he moved, his feet disturbing the ancient surface. He half expected to hear the familiar chink of tumbling pebbles, but the thin atmosphere carried very little sound and his own breathing masked anything he might have heard.

He familiarised himself with his surroundings before flicking on his Head-Up Display. The computer picked out each member of the team and their route plan in a different colour, his own route taking him to a cleft in the rock wall three hundred metres away. The surface of Mars had been swamped by water billions of years ago, and that meant fossilised remains might still exist; it was his job to find them.

He couldn't help but smile. This planet was as far from Earth as anyone had ever ventured, yet to him it felt like home. Mars was a special place - *his* place - and he had never felt more content.

A blur of movement caught his attention and he turned to see a dust devil flit across the floor of the canyon towards him. The storm was small, but powerful enough to scatter a brief hail of dust as it approached.

Tom was enveloped in a cloud of dust, his vision obliterated. He had an overwhelming sense of disorientation, and panicked. His breathing came in rapid gasps, the blood pounding in his ears, and his mouth felt thick as it drained of moisture. A scratchy sensation gagged and choked him as particles cascaded down his throat, and he began to cough. His chest heaved at the imaginary intrusion, and then it was gone.

The storm dwindled quickly in size and Tom coughed one last time as the sensation passed.

With his throat painfully dry, Tom took several sips of water from his drinking tube and closed his eyes while his heartbeat settled. Eventually, he opened his eyes and prepared to move off, chastising himself for his irrational thoughts.

'You fool!' he muttered, embarrassed at his reaction to the dust devil. 'You're a damn fool, Richards; a damn fool and you know it.'

CHAPTER 7

Behind his desk at Mission Control in Houston, Jim Bartlett was becoming more anxious by the minute. The images from the Mars Mission Telescope showed a gradually-worsening situation as storm clouds gathered, dust obliterating the clear skies of Mars. If things progressed the way they had for the past few hours, *Foothold* station could be out of contact for days or even weeks, the storm's intensity severing all communication with the team of astronauts.

'Dave, can you get me some analysis of the height of those clouds, and wind speeds for the area around *Foothold?*'

Dave Foster checked the orbiting communications satellites and clicked his tongue impatiently before responding. 'The storm is passing beneath Guardian 2 now and data is coming in. I'll have an up-date report within the next three minutes.'

'Thanks.' Jim used the time to compress his most recent data, preparing it for a high speed micro-burst transmission, but his headset crackled before he'd finished. 'Jim, it's Dave. I'm sending you some early data now, but you're not gonna like it.'

Jim tapped an icon on his screen and numbers appeared. He frowned, asked the computer to run the data once more and sat back as it ran through. The numbers concerned him and he let out an explosive breath as he activated the comms loop. Brad Knowles, Director of Operations, answered immediately. 'Yes, Jim, what is it?'

Jim cleared his throat before he spoke. 'Brad, I'm sending you my data on the storm that's brewing.' He paused briefly. 'I'm afraid it doesn't look good.'

The first warning came just as EV-1 crested the hill above *Foothold*. The twenty-seven minute time lag between Earth and

Mars made real-time conversation impossible, so communications came compacted into high-speed bursts which were unscrambled by the mission computers. Transmissions usually came every thirty minutes, but this communication was unscheduled.

Jim Bartlett's voice crackled after a journey of more than four hundred million kilometres. '*Foothold*, this is Houston. Sorry to cut in unexpectedly, but we have a situation here which needs your urgent attention. Solar Observatories have monitored an increase in radiation over the past few hours, and now we've picked up an unexpected burst. It's huge.'

Jack heard Jim Bartlett shuffle uncomfortably in his seat. 'By the time you receive this message we should have more information and will be updating you further, but for now we suggest you either prepare for immediate evac to the shelter, or find safe harbour.' Jim's voice dropped a notch as he struggled with a problem about which he could do nothing. 'Sorry fellas, but this is bigger than anyone could have predicted. It's increasing so quickly it could easily jump off the scale.' He took a big breath. 'We have no idea why it's happened – there were no signs. It's a rogue storm.'

Safe harbour. Jack glanced out of the forward windshield to see *Foothold* approaching closer with every second. The crew of EV-1 could be inside the station and safe within the shelter in minutes, but EV-2 could be in trouble if they hadn't received the message from Houston.

Jim's voice ended with a sharp tone of urgency. 'We'll update you again in the next few minutes. Houston out.'

CHAPTER 8

Tom pushed his probe a metre into the surface dust. It sent a burst of high frequency sound deep into the rock beneath his feet, and its results scrolled across the inside of his visor.

The readings registered the presence of hydrated minerals, which indicated water-ice and he moved a few metres before inserting the probe once again. Another reading showed on his visor, the temperatures slightly warmer, but not enough to melt the ice below him.

He frowned and opened his comms channel. 'Hey, you guys. Found anything unusual?'

'A slight temperature rise, but I don't sense any movement or volcanic activity.' Naina cast her eye over the surrounding terrain and sighed. 'It's a puzzle.'

Tom studied the data his probe had returned. 'Yeah, I know what you mean.'

Tiny's voice broke in. 'Patience, my friends. I don't think Mars is ready to give up her secrets just yet. Remember - all good things come to those who wait.'

A gust of wind buffeted the canyon and dust struck their faceplates with gritty taps. It were as though Mars was desperately trying to tell them something, trying to warn them, and as Naina picked up a handful of soil, it cascaded through her gloved fingers. It fell in gritty streams, the slight wind channelled by the steep walls to create a wind tunnel effect. The soil fanned out into a thin blanket. 'Wind's getting up,' she muttered.

'Yeah, I noticed.' Tiny snapped the lid on his samples container shut and dropped it onto the equipment sled. With a nod from Tom, he started the caterpillars and the sled churned over the loose ground. It moved slowly.

The tracks quickly lost their definition as the increasing wind disturbed them. Naina stood transfixed for a moment as the imprints dissipated in the strengthening wind; for some inexplicable reason the sight caused her to feel very uncomfortable.

The wind gusted again. 'Whoa! That was a strong one.' The gust caught Naina's attention and drew her away from her thoughts. She checked the wind speed on the inside of his visor. 'Ninety-six - that's a rise of nine kilometres per hour in the past twenty minutes.' Tom watched her intently as she ran through a series of charts on her Head-Up Display.

'You're the weather specialist. What do you make of it?'

Naina mulled over the readings. 'I'll admit it's uncharacteristic for the time of year; we shouldn't experience winds this strong for another few months, at the very earliest.' She stood thinking, her eyes focused on the graphs projected inside her helmet. 'I think we should proceed carefully, just in case.'

Tom nodded, his helmet barely moving with the gesture. 'Okay, but I need to know immediately if the gusts exceed one hundred and thirty kilometres per hour: that's our safe limit.'

Naina tapped at the keypad on the wrist of her HardSuit, setting her computer to record the wind speed at five second intervals. She spoke as she worked. 'I'm setting my recorder to sound an alert if the wind speed reaches one hundred and twenty. That will give us a safety zone of ten Ks. If it exceeds that I recommend we return to the EV.'

'Agreed.' Tom reached out to tap Tiny on the arm, but before the big man could set the sled in motion a haze of dust particles swarmed around them like bees. A second gust whipped down the canyon and Tom recalled the feel of sand as it stung his skin and clogged his throat.

He tried to swallow but his mouth felt rough with the imagined grittiness. He coughed, the moisture inside his mouth thick, and for an instant couldn't swallow. He felt himself panic again, yet somehow his lips found his drinking tube. Cooling fluid flooded his mouth and he closed his eyes in an effort to calm himself.

When he looked again the swirling cloud had passed, but the oxygen inside his helmet was tainted with an unpleasant aroma. He wrinkled his nose in disgust as he remembered the odour from his dream.

It was sulphur.

EV-1 slowed to a halt outside *Foothold* station and Jack threw his headset down on the console. He'd tried repeatedly to reach his other team but had received no response. Either they were sitting inside a radio hole, or the stormy conditions had prevented them from making contact. He'd also heard nothing from Houston since their last transmission thirty two minutes ago, and that concerned him.

As the EV stood outside the station the crew knew they didn't have much time. With only minutes to prepare for extreme conditions they needed to shut themselves away inside their storm shelter. There was nothing else they could do until radiation levels dropped – however long that took.

Jack could only hope the message from Houston had been picked up by EV-2's crew, and right now he hoped they were scurrying into one of the overhangs which lined the canyon walls. He had no way of knowing if they were safe, and there was nothing he could do to help his friends. It was a very worrying feeling.

Flares of solar radiation coiled outwards from the sun with terrifying ferocity, and Mars warmed in their unexpected attention. Clouds thickened as morning frost quickly evaporated, and dust was dragged with it as the sudden heat caused the thin atmosphere to whirl. Dust was twisted upwards into towering columns, and the clouds sprawled outwards in ever-increasing circles. Their dust-filled tops hung high in the atmosphere as the storm spread quickly to cover more than half the planet, but as more dust rose from the surface on wings of spiralling heat, the balance between uplift and weight became too much.

The storm clouds struck the ground at over four hundred kilometres an hour. They raced westwards, ripping dust from the bedrock, and thrust it into a devastating wall of destruction which barrelled along like a tidal wave.

Seventy kilometres away, shielded by steep inclines, three suited figures worked their way towards a bend in the dry river bed. Oblivious to the ferocity of the approaching storm, they had no idea of what was about to happen.

CHAPTER 9

The wind had peaked at one hundred and ten kilometres per hour and Naina was growing anxious. Her voice struggled against the increasing howl of the storm. 'It may only be an unseasonal dust storm,' she said, her eyes skywards, 'but the cloud cover seems higher than usual. There are some stronger than expected gusts, but... ' Her voice tailed off, her tone unconvincing.

'I know, and I don't like it.' Tom bent backwards as far as his suit would allow and surveyed the sky.

Naina spoke, but another burst of static drowned her words. When it subsided she said, 'I don't understand. With a sudden change in weather patterns this extreme should have been predicted well before now.' Thick clouds of dust enveloped the group again and a small rock fall clattered behind them. 'Something's brewing. Those clouds concern me.'

Tom turned a slow circle, his eyes still raised to the angry sky. 'What happened to all the updates we should have been receiving? Why haven't the Guardians kept us up to speed?'

Tiny didn't respond. 'It could just be a squall,' he said. He flicked through the comms channels but found them filled with static. 'Everything's scrambled,' he said. 'There's nothing coming in or going out.'

'Bad transmitter?' Naina tuned through the channels herself as she spoke but found them the same.

'Can't be,' said Tom. 'We can still speak to each other.' He shook his head in exasperation as the static crackled in his own earpiece. He sighed heavily. 'It's getting worse.'

A strong gust clattered fresh clouds of dust against their HardSuits and the three astronauts rocked slightly in the wind.

Naina checked her read-outs, her voice tight. 'That was a one thirty-two. My computer shows a rise of eight kilometres a minute – no, wait – nearly ten.'

Tom did a quick mental calculation. 'That will put us up to two hundred kilometre winds in under ten minutes. We can't stay out in those conditions,' he said. 'We need to find shelter.' He scanned the steep canyon walls, the bend where they stood evidence of a fast flowing river. The rushing water may have carved something they could use - an overhang, a cave, something to shelter from the increasing wind and driving grit.

Naina projected a canyon map on the inside of her visor and studied it intently. She scrolled it around as she searched. Tiny lowered his binocular visor and scoured the distance frantically while Tom scrambled up the face of the canyon wall. His feet created small avalanches of dust and rock.

'What are you doing?' Tiny's voice crackled through the static. The background noise all but obliterated his words. 'Tom - '

'I've got to get a message off, got to let them know where we are.' Tom paused to take a breath as he continued uphill, his exertion loud in Tiny's earpiece. 'If I can see what's going on above the floor of the canyon we might have a better idea of what we're up against.' His breath rasped and his lips groped for his drinking tube as he climbed. His helmet was fogged over with the exertion. Tom continued regardless; the whirr of his air conditioning fans increased as they worked to keep his suit at a regular temperature.

'What good will it do us? We've got to find somewhere to ride this out now!' Tiny shouted above the static; he knew Tom was making a big mistake.

Naina's voice broke in. 'I think I've found something. It looks like a boulder hole, but we need to move now!' Dust clattered against her HardSuit again, but she didn't notice.

'You two get moving - don't wait for me! I've got to get a message off, but I'll be right down after you.' Tom reached the top of the rise and turned to face them. The wind rocked him where he stood. 'Go!' he shouted.

'You're wrong! Personal safety is more important than radioing our position - you know that! You can send our location after the storm passes.'

'I know, I know. Just give me sixty seconds. If I don't receive a response I'll be right behind you.'

Tiny was angry. 'Riordan'll have you for breakfast over this!' He watched his friend and then turned away. In his ears Tom's voice called into the strengthening wind.

'*Foothold*, this is Richards. Winds are strengthening to dangerous levels. We're taking shelter within the Valles Marineris. Suit identification beacons are on. We're not receiving comms on any channel and don't know if you're receiving this. Will try contacting you again when conditions allow.'

Tom staggered as the wind blasted him. He was concerned at its ferocity. *It shouldn't be like this*, he thought. *This is way beyond anything we trained for.*

The storm gripped the bulky form of his HardSuit and he stumbled as the surface beneath him gave way. His feet sank as the edge crumbled and he lunged forward, reaching out for the safety of a large boulder. His gloved hands gripped its pitted surface as the wind blasted again and he pulled himself upright. His feet slipped again and he struggled to regain his footing.

Tom shouted above the noise of the wind as it scoured across his helmet. 'Our current position puts us at least three Ks from...' His voice faltered mid-sentence as he peered across the horizon, unsure of what he had seen as the dust clouds momentarily separated. He stared hard across the plain and felt his throat begin to constrict as the scene built itself out of the murk.

Across the eastern horizon a column of cloud spiralled high into the Martian sky. Its height was so great that it vanished from sight, its edges blanketing the far horizon.

Tom stood motionless, his body frozen by the sight. The storm front covered the open ground in seconds; distant hill ranges vanished from sight as they were smothered by the approaching wall.

Tom knew there was nothing anyone could do to save them.

CHAPTER 10

EV-1 stood alongside airlock B, connected to *Foothold* by an umbilical tunnel. The vehicle stood empty as Jack, Frank and Irina scurried around inside the station.

A thin flurry of dust wafted around their feet, disturbed by their hurried movements. Even with outer and inner airlocks, red dust had always found its way into the habitation module.

Jack studied the most recent weather charts from the orbiting Guardians. The data was just under an hour old, but better than nothing. He stood with his fists bunched on the workstation as he hunched over the numbers.

Frank clattered around as he prepared the emergency shelter, while Irina stowed their most recent rock samples: as chief geologist she was very protective of her rocks, and their newest sample was of particular interest. She placed the sample case which bore the tag M08-427 carefully onto a packed shelf and stopped briefly to rest her hand on the lid of the container. From the moment she had seen its markings she hadn't been able to get the possibilities out of her mind. They were mind-blowing.

Jack's shout brought her up with a jolt and she ran for the stairs, her body moving quickly in the low Martian gravity. Frank met her in the hatchway as he made his way back towards the comms station.

'Ce ne semble pas bon.'

'Hmm?' Naina looked at Frank. She didn't speak French.

'I said, it doesn't look good,' Frank grumbled, his accented English thick and disgruntled. He only slipped into his native tongue when he was anxious or excited.

Jack's face was white in the reflected glow of the illuminated map table. He was listening to a communication from Houston; the voice came in waves, drowned by layers of heavy static.

'. . .*of unprecedented strength . . . planet wide blanket coverage . . .*

26

higher than . . .recorded . . .wave front . . .kilometres per hour, repeat nine hundred plus kilometres per hour . . . advise . . .now . . .'

The voice was drowned out once more, the static total. Jack flicked through the autoband frequencies but the result was unchanged.

Jack stood up. 'We have to move now - we can't afford to wait any longer. Lord knows how much radiation we've taken already.'

He glanced at his dosimeter, relieved to see it showed his radiation exposure was within safe limits, but raised his eyebrows at how dark it had become.

'What about EV-2 – any news from them?' Irina held her headset to one ear and tuned through the frequencies herself. 'We can't leave them out there. What if they don't know? If they were out of contact with us, then chances are they haven't heard from Houston either.'

Jack scratched at the nape of his neck. He shook his head. 'I haven't been able to raise them. All I get is static.' His voice was tight, stress making his words short and clipped. They were his friends as well. 'We can only hope Houston has had more success.'

'But we have to try and warn them.' Irina's voice showed her desperation.

He placed his hand on her shoulder and squeezed gently. 'There's nothing we can do. We have to get to the shelter - we've got to think of ourselves for the moment. That's what they'll be doing right now – looking for shelter.' *I hope*, he added silently, and then stepped towards the open hatch. 'Every second we wait brings that storm closer, and if it's travelling as fast as Houston predicts, then it's almost here.' He paused, looking up as something clattered above them. The wind rubbed against the outer walls of their habitat and something creaked. It was a sound they had not heard before.

'Right. Secure all hatches. Grab anything you think you'll need and get to the shelter. Let's go.' Jack moved to the science station and set the weather sensors to begin recording. If the storm were as big as NASA had predicted, they had to collect as much data as possible. *Naina will never forgive me if I miss this opportunity,* he thought. *I just hope she makes it back...*

'Come on.' Frank's voice was urgent as he held the hatch open. He wanted to bolt it and run for the shelter, but Jack continued to fiddle with the science station settings. 'Jack, come *on!*' he hissed.

With a final glance at the monitors, Jack turned and ducked through the low hatch. *What will we come back to?* he thought, as Frank pulled the hatch closed. *Will there be anything at all left for us to return to?*

She made her way quickly towards the observation blister. Large enough for one person at a time - two at a squash if any crew member didn't mind close company – it was designed to give a 360° view of the world beyond. Its use was limited, on account of the radiation levels that bombarded Mars on a daily basis, but Irina often stayed longer than she should. As long as she kept a close eye on her exposure levels, she would be okay.

Irina loved the solitude it offered. So far from home, she felt an affinity with the world outside. It was a world as uncompromising and harsh as anywhere she could wish to be, but sitting here immersed in its beauty, it allowed her a degree of relaxation in the artificial world of the station. Being cooped up in a tin can over four hundred million kilometres from home was enough to drive anybody stir-crazy. She needed somewhere to escape to, somewhere to sit and watch the world turn, just for a while.

On a world more alien than anywhere humanity had ever set foot, it made her feel strangely human.

Irina poked her head up into the hatchway and instantly sensed something was amiss. The light level was different; the soft, dusky light was wrong for the time of day. She should know, she'd spent many an evening watching the sun disappear behind the distant mountains: it had always been a beautiful experience. Her hand gripped the hatch tightly, her head inside the bubble as she surveyed the scene. Everything was coated in a soft yellow sheen as the reflected light of the Martian day cast itself over grey metal and white plastic, but the staccato tap of dust against the dome increased in tempo and volume with every passing second.

To her right a mass of low cloud whipped past, the dome's surface scratched by the grittiness of the dust. Swirling currents were clearly visible in its thickness and she looked closer. *No, that's not cloud,* she thought, *that's sand!*

Stepping into the bubble she moved towards the dome. Beyond it sand flew horizontally; thick cords of yellow, orange and red twisted upon themselves as the clouds streamed across the barren landscape.

Irina had witnessed dust storms before. She had watched in trepidation the first time a dust devil had whirled towards her. The tortured column of dust had fixated her professional interest, but had hit the station and simply dissipated, its thin wisps fading to nothing. The experience had excited and terrified her in equal measure, and she remembered wondering what would have happened if it had been significantly larger.

Irina laid a hand on the dome's cool surface, mesmerised by the ribbons of dust as they merged and separated. The strange patterns were hypnotic in the dim light, but she knew something about them wasn't right.

The dust before her suddenly vanished, layers of bedrock exposed for the briefest of instants, and she frowned. *Bedrock? But this area has a deep layer of sand. That's why we chose to build...*

The dust resumed its streaming, its speed faster than before, and she realised what was wrong. She swallowed but her throat caught and she coughed. 'Oh, my God,' she said as she stepped back from the blister. 'The sand's not being blown, it's being *pulled!*' The dust clouds parted again and the bedrock was laid bare for long seconds, its heavily lined layers of volcanic rock fashioned into smooth curves and swirls by an age of erosion.

It was a brief glimpse of Martian history she had not expected to see, and in her moment of stunned disbelief something made her look up.

She wished she hadn't.

CHAPTER 11

In seconds it was almost upon him, yet Tom remained entranced by the storm's approach. It quickly filled the whole of his vision, twisting and writhing upon itself in a nightmare of anger and violence. Its magnitude sapped his strength and he shrank back inside his HardSuit. Tears welled in his eyes - whether tears of fear or tears of wonder, he would never know.

Logic told him the storm would be no more powerful than an Earthly squall, Mars' atmosphere being only thick enough to generate a slight breeze, yet some deep-rooted sense of self-preservation jolted his body into motion.

In the seconds before the storm hit, Tom was aware of every particle of dust, every rattle and clatter as it was sucked towards the approaching storm. Then all was silent, the sound of his own breathing loud in his ears as the wave front towered above him.

Its violence took him by surprise. Lifted clear of the rocky surface he felt himself thrown backwards, his body twisted and enveloped by the dust. The world around him vanished in a swirl of red while the particles struck his suit like heavy rain on a tin roof.

The rock appeared suddenly, its sharp, angular face knife-like in the swirling redness, and he felt the impact on his visor. His world shattered into razor-sharp fragments as his cheekbone smashed against metal, and his face went numb. Precious oxygen was torn violently from his lungs to whip away like snow in the howling wind, and he tried desperately to inhale, but there was nothing to breathe. The thin atmosphere was full of dust, and as he began to choke his HardSuit attempted to compensate for the loss of pressure, but the effort was futile.

With consciousness ebbing away, Tom found himself leaning precariously over the canyon edge. His gloves probed frantically at his broken visor, but could find no way in. His mouth and throat filled with dust, and he started to retch as sand scratched at his face; it clogged his nostrils and sealed his eyes shut, and consciousness slipped away. The faces of those he loved filled his last moments of existence, and he thought especially of Annie.

Tears brimmed in his eyes one final time, and a single thought engulfed his fading consciousness.

This is it. Time to go.

CHAPTER 12

Irina was in the hatchway when the storm hit. The station rocked under the assault and she was thrown painfully against the rim of the hatch, but managed to pull it closed over her head as the dome above was ripped from the station. The sudden loss of pressure pulled violently at the hatch, and it juddered against the bulkhead, but remained shut as she pulled down on it with all her strength.

Looking up, Irina could see there was no way of engaging the locking mechanism without releasing one hand. Her muscles complained and she knew exhaustion would soon cause her to give in, but if she let go she would die. That much was certain, yet she had no other option.

The hatch juddered noisily against the bulkhead again and she slumped down against the ladder, her weight dragging the hatch against the seals. She hooked her legs into the rungs of the ladder for leverage, and hoped she had enough downward force to hold the hatch closed while she attempted to lock it. It was all she had. It had to work.

She dropped her weight as low as possible and readied herself. Ignoring the painful forces on her shoulder, elbow and wrist, she released her right hand and lunged at the locking handle.

It didn't move; she didn't have enough leverage. Sweat stung her eyes and she wiped her face on her sleeve as she yanked on the handle again, but the air around her began escaping in short bursts. Screaming in agonised anger, Irina pulled downwards again. Fear gave her new strength and she gripped the hatch more tightly, her knuckles white as the hatch sealed itself.

'*Bozhe!*' she screamed. 'Come on! Stay shut! Stay shut!' She pulled harder and something snapped in her shoulder. She cried out, but did not lessen her downward pull. Putting back her head, she closed her eyes and cried out. '*Not like this! Please! No!*'

The hatch juddered once more. '*No!*'

The locking mechanism clunked home and something warm folded itself over her fingers. A smell of sweat invaded her nostrils and she opened her eyes to see a white mission uniform, *Louville* stitched into the fabric above the left breast in dark blue thread. He slipped his arm around her back while he coaxed her fingers from the handle. 'Come on,' he said. 'It's locked. You're safe.'

Frank's fingers peeled at her tightly coiled hands and teased them from the cold metal, finger by finger. Irina slumped to the base of the ladder and lay there, her lungs heaving with exertion, but Frank dragged her to her feet. 'We have to go,' he said. 'We have to get to the shelter. Can you walk?'

'I think so.' She staggered forward and his arms enveloped her, his support more necessary than she realised. Within seconds they were in the corridor, and Irina soon found herself in the central causeway of the station.

Frank urged her on. 'Come on! Faster!' He led her along the gantry which encircled the interior of the station, and they quickly descended a ladder to the open shelter below.

Jack's head poked through the open hatchway. 'We have to close up! Hurry!'

Irina stumbled and caught her foot on the rim as she climbed through. She spilled untidily into the cramped space, Jack's expression grim as he grabbed her and lowered her into a seat.

Frank slammed the hatch and twisted the heavy bolts into place. He stood, his hands frozen to the hatch as pressurised air shrieked into the shelter. The noise was deafening, but soon fell silent, and he slumped against the ladder in relief.

A familiar voice called his name, but he did not respond immediately. When it called again he opened his eyes and turned slowly.

'*Spasibo.*' Irina's voice was trembling and thick with tears as she touched him lightly on his shoulder. '*Spasibo,*' she said. 'Thank you.'

CHAPTER 13

Jim Bartlett banged his fist on the console, his insides churning knots of fear and worry as monitor screens around him flickered with constant updates. While the solar flare wasn't directly affecting Earth, data transmissions towards Mars had been totally disrupted. The levels of solar radiation currently being thrown out by the sun would consume any transmission, the way an ocean would swallow a drop of rainwater, and the astronauts would have no idea of the severity of the storm.

Bill Marshall steepled his fingers and blew out a long sigh as his monitor refreshed itself again. He pulled up fresh images from the Mars Mission Telescope and studied them closely.

Running the images as a time-lapse movie he watched Mars swirl itself into a tortured version of Hell. The arms of a twenty thousand kilometre wide storm spiralled across the surface at increasing speed. He shook his head in disbelief.

Jim Bartlett looked over Bill's shoulder, his eyes fixed to the screen in disbelief. 'Have you seen these figures?' he asked. The solar flare had churned out more radiation in a single burst than the combined output of the past ten flares. He slumped into his own chair and studied the figures: it was a storm of monstrous proportions.

'I know. I'm looking at them now.' Jim converted the figures to a chart and whistled as spikes revealed themselves. 'Have you seen what it's doing to the atmosphere? Radiation levels, wind speeds, they're unbelievable! I hope those guys found shelter before this lot hit.'

The probability of dead astronauts on another world was not something Jim wanted to discuss. 'Their shelter isn't designed to cope with radiation levels of this magnitude,' he said, 'but they're carrying good shielding. If they made it inside early enough...'

Jim laced his fingers behind his head. 'Yeah,' he said quietly, 'Yeah, I know.'

Both men watched the data as it flickered across their screens, and looked at new images as they surged into the system. The whole situation seemed unreal. Jim's mind whirled as he struggled to understand how a storm this big, this powerful, could present itself with no warning. Studies of the sun meant solar flares were predictable within an eleven year cycle, and even then the sun gave between twelve and twenty four hours' warning before a solar eruption, but the sun was only half way through that cycle. It didn't make sense.

One of the reasons the mission had launched nearly eighteen months ago was to safeguard the astronauts from high doses of radiation. By having them operate at the lowest point of the solar cycle it gave them the surest guarantee of safety. But here they were, with a solar flare of lethal proportions, and there was nothing anyone could do about it.

The world had come to know the first Martian explorers more intimately than any other person in history – their backgrounds, their personalities, their hopes for the mission - but now they were probably dead. It was a painful realisation the world would struggle to deal with.

A voice broke into his thoughts. 'Bill, which view are you looking at?'

'Equatorial. Why?'

'Take a look at the polar view. Tell me what you see.'

Bill pulled up the menu for the planet's surface. 'Okay. What am I looking for?'

'Go to atmospheric analysis and play back the past hour's results.'

Bill hunched over his monitor as numbers flickered past. A graph spiked across his screen; its colours indicated a whole range of chemicals in the atmosphere. 'I see carbon dioxide, nitrogen, argon, oxygen, water, a few other trace elements, nothing unusual but...' He stopped. 'That can't be right.'

He tapped a few keys and most of the graph vanished. Only

red and blue spikes remained and he studied them closely. 'If I'm reading this right – and it must be wrong; this data *has* to be scrambled – then hydrogen-oxygen combinations have risen steeply in the past ninety minutes.'

'What do you make of it?' Jim studied his colleague; waited for him to pick up some error in calculation, something he'd missed, but his interpretation of the data was the same as Bill's.

'According to this, the atmosphere is soaking up incredible amounts of water vapour.' He paused to check his data once more. 'But there's only one source on the planet large enough to account for readings like these.'

He sat back, stunned. 'The ice caps are melting!'

CHAPTER 14

Tears streamed down Tiny's face as he dragged Tom's HardSuit over the rocky floor of the ravine. He kicked out at a fist sized rock which blocked his path, his pace never faltering as he fought his way towards the equipment sled.

Tom's broken visor stared up at him like an open wound as he leant against the sled for breath.

In his grief, Tiny rounded on his friend. 'What did you go and do that for? Why couldn't you just get yourself to shelter like the rest of us?' Tiny desperately needed to rub his eyes but couldn't. 'Aw, man, why did you have to go and push things too far?'

He grabbed Tom's suit by its harness and lugged him onto the sled. In the low gravity Tom wasn't heavy, but Tiny lost his balance and tumbled forwards. He broke his fall by grabbing Tom's suit. He stared for a moment at the sand-clogged face behind the broken visor, and his anger welled again. 'You *stupid* man! Why didn't you just come when I asked you to?' He shook his head. 'What am I going to tell your sister now? I promised her I'd make sure you came back without a scratch. Jeepers, man, she'll *never* marry me now!'

Grief and anger gave way to duty. 'Well, I'm gonna get you back to *Foothold*, no matter what. You're not staying out here. I'm taking you home.'

Naina's voice crackled through his headset, but the combination of static and the clatter of sand and grit against his helmet obliterated most of her message.

He turned his volume to maximum and listened. Naina's voice had vanished into the background hiss. He made his way towards a group of boulders, and as the wind lessened he saw her wave.

For an instant Naina didn't know which of the two figures was on the sled, then Tiny's black helmet appeared out of the gloom.

Her legs went numb and she caught her breath.

Tiny approached and touched his helmet to hers. 'Naina, help me!'

She faltered when she saw the broken visor, its jagged edges stark against the smooth detail of his helmet. 'Oh no,' she said quietly. 'Oh no.'

Tiny gripped the harness on Tom's suit again and heaved the body upright. 'Help me, Naina. We have to get under cover.'

Between them they dragged Tom's body up a sharp incline. The surface slid away under their weight and they stumbled, the wind threatening to blow them over as they fought their way to the top.

An opening barely wide enough for two was set back from the incline, and Tiny forced Tom's body inside it. He sagged against the wall of the opening and gasped for breath.

Grit clattered against their HardSuits. Tiny looked into Naina's visor and saw his own reflection superimposed over her distress. 'Later... tell you later,' he mumbled.

Naina gripped Tom's suit again and moved deeper inside, but Tiny urged her forward. 'Not here - can't stop here. Too close. Have to get as far in as we can. Have to go as deep as we can.'

Tiny's behaviour spooked Naina as he moved into the depths of the cave. 'What's happened? What's going on?' She followed him, then stopped and looked into the shadows of his face. 'What haven't you told me?'

Tiny ignored her. Switching on his helmet lamps he cast their beams about in the darkness. It was the first time artificial light had ever touched the rocks. Their colours had not been eroded by the elements, and were filled with fine bands of red and orange. They were quite beautiful.

'Deeper - get deeper. You're too close there!'

'Tiny, what's going on? Tell me!'

He stopped for a moment and rested his aching muscles. Naina stepped around and grabbed his suit by its straps. 'What's going on?' she repeated. 'Tell me!'

'Radiation,' he said. 'Radiation levels are high.'

Naina tapped at the panel on her arm. A digital display flashed up inside her visor and she felt her blood run cold. It showed a dark grey bar where it should have been yellow, her radiation dosage dangerously high.

Another chill ran through her. 'But you've been out in the storm longer than I have. If my levels are elevated then yours must be...Tiny, how much radiation have you taken?'

Tiny didn't reply. He'd heard his computer beep at him when he was still in the open. It had attempted to warn him of his exposure levels, but he hadn't had time to check it.

Tiny's voice was small, filled with grief, and his emotions blanked out Naina's voice. 'Perhaps he fell,' he said. 'Perhaps the wind blew him, caused him to lose his balance.' He looked at Naina. Tears filled his eyes. 'I just don't know.'

'How much?' Naina was frantic, but Tiny didn't answer. She banged her gloved hand on the top of his helmet.

He blinked. Tears ran down his face.

'How much? What's your exposure?'

Tiny smiled with an expression of quiet acceptance. 'I don't know. I don't think it matters now anyway.'

Naina plugged her data cable into Tiny's HardSuit. It relayed his medical data onto her visor: heart rate, blood pressure and radiation levels. Naina began to shake as she read Tiny's chart.

It was close to the lethal range.

CHAPTER 15

It was a beautiful day. Tom turned his face towards the sun, its warmth blissful. His skin tingled. It felt fantastic, and he smiled.

He strolled along the riverbank and stopped to dangle his legs in the water. Its coolness flowed gently around his ankles and he sighed as the sensation soothed him.

A shadow blocked the sunlight, its features elusive. 'Delightful, isn't it?' The figure spoke, its voice was quiet and calming, yet its tone gave no indication of age or accent. 'Mind if I join you?'

'Please do.' Tom shielded his eyes as the figure lowered itself onto the grass beside him and dipped its feet into the stream.

'Oh, that feels good...' The figure sighed and sloshed its feet around in the cool water.

Tom nodded. 'It's what summers are made for. I spent hours paddling in streams when I was a boy – I went home soaked through more times than I can remember.'

The memory was clear, as though the events had happened only yesterday. 'I had this thing about trying to dam the flow of water.' He laughed at the memory. 'Never managed it, though. Somehow the water always found a way through: a small crack here, a tiny hole there. It was as if it challenged me, as if it had a life of its own.'

'It always finds a way through,' said the other man.

Tom agreed. 'It's a funny thing, water. It supports life, yet it can take it away. Look at the Sahara desert and the polar ice caps: they weren't always like that. The Sahara was once an oasis of life, the arctic a tropical zone. But now...' Tom raised his hands. 'Life has vanished.'

Both men sat in silence, lost in their own thoughts. Eventually the older man turned and placed his feet on the grass between them, his face still shrouded in shadow. When he spoke his voice had taken on a familiar tone.

'Time is like water.'

'Time?'

The man nodded. 'It flows effortlessly, folding around those it meets. We are all affected by its passing, yet can do nothing to stop it. It flows through everything we do.' The old man paused. 'Time is powerful, as is water. They are the backbone of existence.'

'I suppose you're right.' Tom nodded as he mulled the words over. 'I like that. What you've said makes sense. Thank you.'

The old man smiled. 'You're welcome, Tom.'

It took a few seconds for Tom to register he had been called by name. He looked closer, but could only make out a white shirt and dark hat. Somehow the silhouette seemed familiar; like a fragment of a memory. 'Do I know you from somewhere?'

'Oh, you haven't seen me since you were a boy.' The man's smile went unseen in the shadows.

'But I don't...wait, there's something about you, something familiar.' He moved to one side and looked hard into the shadows. Dark eyes stared back at him, but the shadows were dense and he could make out only a little detail. 'I'm sorry. You have me at a bit of a disadvantage. What did you say your name was?'

'I didn't, but you do know me. We have met several times, and I've been with you for a long time.'

'What do you mean?'

'Tom, do I really look that different?'

Tom shook his head. 'I...'

'Come now. Think back to your childhood; to the experiences which changed your life. Think back, think deep.'

Memories stirred and Tom shifted anxiously. 'Mr Lampard?'

The old man made an agreeable noise. 'That name will do.'

Memories of their first meeting flooded back: his sister Abi in the library, enveloped in a mass of shifting light; the terrifying encounter with the An'Tsari ship and Mr Lampard's voice deep within his mind.

But there was something else: a feeling that he had carried

with him from that day, a feeling of never quite being alone.

'You've been with me all these years. You've been watching me, haven't you?'

'Guiding you, shall we say. I had a duty to keep you safe.'

'From what?'

'From those mishaps of childhood, those moments of danger which may have taken you away. They could not be allowed to happen.'

Tom sat for a moment as a terrifying memory flooded back. 'I should have died, but I didn't. That was you, wasn't it?'

Mr. Lampard's voice was warm. 'Look inside yourself. You already know the answer.'

'But it's not just that, is it? You've been with me all along. Why?'

'You were too important to lose.'

'Me?' Tom laughed.

'Come. I will show you.' Mr. Lampard stood and indicated for Tom to join him.

The summer day was replaced by the familiarity of his childhood home, and the vision hit him hard.

He stepped onto the staircase, immediately aware of the loose floorboard three steps from the top and the step which had always creaked.

He smiled at the memory and followed the rail as he descended the staircase, never once lifting his hand. Its familiar smoothness ended in a decorative shell which spiralled away to nothing at the bottom of the staircase; a beautiful swirl of polished wood which had always held a strange fascination for him. He had run his hands over it so many times as a child, and as he did so again its smoothness rekindled long forgotten memories of home.

Voices beyond the kitchen door drew his attention and he pulled it open to peer through. His heart lurched.

Mum and Dad sat round the kitchen table with the whole family, Christmas lunch laid before them like a king's banquet.

Turkey with all the trimmings: Christmas in the Richards household, a family tradition he remembered with longing. Christmas had always been a big event but now, as he stared at a moment in time, his heart sagged. It was a memory he did not wish to revisit, and he turned away.

They opened onto a different scene. 'I don't believe it - this is my old room. My things.' He gazed around in wonder, his face split by a wide grin. A *Star Wars* poster hung above his bed, one corner flapping gently in the breeze from the open window, the sticky tape having turned brittle and lost its adhesion as it dried out in the summer heat.

Above his desk hung a signed football shirt, a Get Well Soon gift from the Middlesbrough players after an accident that had nearly claimed his life. Players had visited him in hospital, bringing him the signed shirt, and it was a gift he'd treasured since. He touched the frame and felt a shiver, a memory of the event which had nearly killed him chilling him momentarily.

'This is nothing but a trip down memory lane – '

Mr. Lampard shrugged. 'It is a frozen moment in time.'

Tom climbed wearily to his feet. The emotion drained him. 'So why did you bring me here?'

'I needed you to see things that you would remember, memories that you would accept.' He spoke quietly and slowly. 'Memories that would prepare you for the things to come.'

'Things to come? What things?'

'These.'

He was ten years old again. Tom watched himself sleep, covered in a thin sheet against the summer night, while the bedroom window stood wide open to encourage the slightest wisp of cooling breeze.

Although asleep, the young boy sensed a mind inside his own; a faint voice in the darkness which faded in and out like a radio in the night time.

Tom watched the scene unfold, and heard words for the second time in his life:

The knowledge you possess will ensure our time in the universe – the accumulation of our knowledge, our experiences and our existence – will not end as the stars must end. The universe must know its origins. It must know from where it came. And it must continue.

The sleeping boy's mind responded to the words, his question filled with wonder.

What can I do? I am only a child. No-one will believe me.

The voice continued.

When the time is right they will. You will understand.

Understand what?

A pause, as if something waiting to be said were being held back.

You will find it.

Find what?

Silence.

Mr Lampard?

Silence.

'Now do you remember?'

Tom struggled to grasp the conversation he had just heard, his reply faint. 'Yes. Yes, I remember.'

'Good. Then we have an understanding.'

'An understanding? About what?' Everything confused him.

'It will make sense soon enough.'

Tom lowered himself slowly onto the bed next to his younger self. He watched as the boy slept on, unaware of what was to happen and the way his life would soon change.

Mr Lampard beckoned. 'There is more. Come.' He opened the door and stepped through.

CHAPTER 16

Twin suns cast long double shadows across the stony ground as they rose above the horizon, and a sweet scent assailed his nostrils. It reminded him of honeysuckle, and home.

Shielding his eyes from the glare, Tom turned a slow circle. He gazed open mouthed at the tall, irregular columns which towered majestically above him, their wide bases tapering skywards from the rocky landscape to vanish in the clouds high above. Tom felt insignificant as they towered above. The landscape was distorted as though disturbed by underground movement, its surface folded into great peaks and troughs. *Volcanic activity*, thought Tom. *So like Earth.*

He squinted as he faced the twin suns, their light brighter now as the burning discs rose higher into the morning sky. Their warmth soaked his skin but he knew the day was only young; the heat would become more intense as the morning wore on.

Mr. Lampard appeared comfortable in the surroundings, the light and heat expected. 'My apologies,' he said, his tone sincere. 'We require a high level of light and warmth. It nourishes our bodies, but you find it less appealing.' Tom squinted at Mr. Lampard, his form almost ghostly in the brightness. The old man held up his hand and the light levels dimmed. For the first time Tom saw Mr. Lampard clearly, and was surprised that he appeared not to have aged.

Around them was a scene of beauty. A range of distant mountains covered the horizon, their lofty peaks high above the rolling lowlands, while sprawling forests cast cool shadows of blue and purple across the hillside. The scene was Earth-like, yet strangely different. If not for the double suns which hung low in the pale sky, and the sculpted columns of rock which dwarfed the landscape, Tom might have still believed he was on his home world.

But something was different. The undulations which creased the world vanished as the ground fell away into a wide basin. Within it, concentric circles and lines intersected each other as vast patterns sprawled across the valley floor. From his vantage point Tom could see only a foreshortened view, but felt something familiar about their arrangement.

Tom's head ached and his eyes throbbed, the sensation similar to the vibrations he remembered while resting his head against the window of his parents' moving car as a boy. The rhythm was trance-like, but after a while it became uncomfortable and Tom rubbed at his neck.

'The vibrations you feel will not harm you,' said Mr. Lampard. 'They are a living force from deep within the core of this planet. They run through every blade of grass, every tree and every rock. They are an energy that provides growth and healing, and are unique to our world.'

Tom rubbed his temples. He bent to pick at the fine grass, rolling the blades between his fingers and brought them to his nose. They released a sweet aroma, their effect immediately easing his headache.

'Honeysuckle.' Tom smiled at Mr. Lampard. 'It's honeysuckle.'

'Almost.'

Tom smiled. 'It reminds me of when I was a boy. We had

honeysuckle growing across the front of our home.' He remembered the way the bees had loved it. And his Mum. 'This is so beautiful,' he said, 'but where are we?'

Mr. Lampard sat down and gazed longingly across the valley before them. 'A place long gone. A world of memories.' He sat for a moment before continuing. 'This is the place of your origin. The world from which your – from which *our* - seed once sprung.'

An almost-memory flooded Tom's mind, but vanished before he could grasp its significance. It left a vague echo and Tom realised he had almost understood something of importance. It was as though the dam of his childhood memories was straining to hold back a great outpouring, attempting to restrict the flow to a trickle, when the full force of it struck him. He gasped at the truth.

'You...I...we are the same. That's it, isn't it? We originated from here, from this world.'

Tom saw the same smile he had seen in the library a lifetime ago, the kind smile of a man whose origin was different to his own. Or was it?

'I once told you that when the time was right you would understand. That time has come.' Mr. Lampard stood, his arms spread. 'Welcome to the cradle of life; the world where all existence began.'

Tom was stunned at the revelation. 'So, what is this world?'

'We named the planet *An'Tsa*. It means *Life*.' Mr. Lampard gazed out at the distant hills. When he spoke his voice was full of longing and Tom realised the world maintained some kind of hold over Mr. Lampard.

The old man continued. 'This planet was my home, a beautiful world of land and sky. It was the only living place within the universe.' His expression changed to one of sadness and loss, almost of regret. 'But we felt called by the stars and outgrew this planet, our cradle, as all children must eventually do.'

'Where did you go?'

'Everywhere. We explored, but found the universe to be

devoid of life. When we finally returned home we found our own world was dying and knew our existence could not be allowed to fade. It was our duty to survive.'

'So, you seeded yourself.'

Mr. Lampard sighed. 'Yes, but our attempts were not as successful as we had intended.'

Tom pondered Mr. Lampard's words but did not question them. *Not yet,* he thought. He indicated the slight incline of the hill before them. 'Shall we walk? I would like to see more of your world.' He strode off, more relaxed than he had felt for days.

They approached a spring which bubbled from the hillside, its water crystal clear, the sight refreshing, and Tom bent to take a drink. Mr. Lampard stood over him, and for a moment a shadow draped across his shoulders like a cloak of dark emotion. Tom had a sense Mr. Lampard was hiding something from him and he shivered, but as soon as the old man moved away the sensation lifted.

Mr. Lampard glanced briefly at Tom and smiled, his expression pleasant and warming before he turned his back and stared out to the distant horizon. Without a word he raised his hand, and the world faded.

A warm glow parted the darkness. It was the familiar yellow light of Earth, but subtly altered.

A world of unimaginable beauty appeared as the sun rose, its colours a brightening palette against the darkness, and Tom's thoughts turned instantly to his mother. She had loved to watch the sunrise, often standing alone in the garden while the sun's first rays crept over the horizon, the sunbeams parting the darkness as the world turned. It had been her moment, and he realised how much he missed her, but could not allow his feelings to surface again. Not now.

Somehow Tom knew he wasn't on Earth – he didn't know how he knew, he could see very little other than the distant horizon as the sun's rays spilled over it - but the scene had a different feel.

Waves lapped gently against his toes and calm descended once again as the light and warmth worked its magic. He looked around, expecting to see the figure of Mr. Lampard by the water's edge, but found he was alone. Strangely he didn't feel worried; the water trickling over his toes bewitched him, and he knew Mr. Lampard would not be far.

He was on a smaller world than Earth. The horizon was closer - the curve of the planet more pronounced against the sky – and the landscape was sparsely vegetated with a reddish-green layer of plant life as far as he could see. A single star climbed slowly above the horizon, its disc about the same diameter as Earth's sun. He held out his thumb to cover it. *Single yellow dwarf star. Similar distance than Earth's sun. Interesting.* He folded his arms as he considered his surroundings. *Where are we?*

Walking inland Tom crested a small hill, the grass beneath his feet more coarse than that of Earth, each blade broader for its length. He crouched, picked a handful and absent-mindedly thumbed it into a ball as a lazy shroud of mist parted to reveal a tantalising glimpse of the valley below. The mist thinned further and the hairs on the back of his neck prickled as a vast cleft appeared. It ran from horizon to horizon, its stunning beauty familiar, but his mind refused to accept the world before him. His heart told him it was real, but he knew it could only be a vision created by Mr. Lampard. It stunned him nevertheless.

Why this vision? What does it mean?

Tom watched transfixed as the final wisps of cloud thinned to nothing and a giant volcanoe appeared. He closed his eyes against the towering sight, but the image had burnt itself forever into his mind, and he could not deny the truth.

Mars!

Tom's spirits soared, and when at last he opened his eyes he found his vision distorted by a veil of tears. He blinked them away and stared in wonder as the largest of Mars' volcanoes rose before him. It towered high into the morning sky, and from that moment on Tom Richards knew that nothing in his life would ever be the same again.

CHAPTER 17

After the luxury of the living space above, the shelter was claustrophobic. Even the habitation module seemed large by comparison.

The shelter was equipped with emergency rations and water to last a crew of six for two months. With only three occupants they realised how cramped it would have been had they all been inside the shelter, and after only twenty-four hours the ration packs already seemed tasteless.

Irina sighed with boredom. She lay on her bunk, head pillowed on her arm as she traced the outline of the wall panels with a lazy finger. Her final moments with the hatch had replayed themselves repeatedly over the long days, and the sickening crack as the observation blister had been ripped away had haunted her dreams every night. They were a chilling reminder of human frailty, and Irina shuddered at what would have happened had Frank not reached her in time.

The mission had called for the careful matching of individual personalities, but how could anyone ever have prepared them for a scenario in which half the team was wiped out in a single event? Mission failure had been discussed, but when the moment had arrived, the reality had been devastating.

Irina's thoughts turned inwards for the millionth time, but could find no answer to the question that had burned relentlessly inside everyone's mind.

Will we survive this?

CHAPTER 18

Disorientated, Tom gradually became aware of his surroundings as the smell of dust and polish invaded his senses. He knew instinctively where he was, but how long had it been?

'Thirty one years. You were ten when we first met.'

'Ten.' Tom repeated the word as if it were a foreign word on his tongue. 'Ten. Yes, I remember.'

Mr. Lampard sat alongside Tom. The wooden chair creaked as he moved. 'Your time will soon come. Then you will understand.' Tom frowned, but Mr. Lampard interrupted his thoughts. 'Time is short. You must listen.'

'When we first arrived, your solar system was new and many of your planets were not fully formed. It was as though our past whispered to us through the worlds that orbited your sun, and we were overwhelmed to find them so like the planet we had left behind. Your worlds called to us like an echo of our past.'

'Go on.'

'That pleased us greatly,' said Mr. Lampard, 'and we knew that from then on, events would be different.'

'How?'

Mr. Lampard pursed his lips before speaking. 'In every universe we had encountered there had only ever been one planet with the potential for life to evolve. But in your universe we found two.'

'Earth and Mars,' Tom said. The planet he had witnessed, the abundance of life thriving upon its surface, all made sense. His voice was thick with excitement. 'The planet you showed me was Mars.'

Mr. Lampard shifted in his seat. His gaze was nervous, distracted, like that of a young child caught misbehaving by its mother. He placed his hands between his knees and hunched his shoulders, rocking slightly on his seat. It was a human trait; Tom wondered where it had originated.

'What?' Tom sat straighter on his seat. 'What aren't you telling me?'

Mr. Lampard's voice was nervous. 'It is hard to admit failure.'

'Failure? Why...what happened? What went wrong?'

Mr. Lampard rubbed the side of his face; his stubble sounded coarse against his palm. 'We found two planets orbiting your sun in almost identical orbits. They were similar in composition – and both were perfect. Each was capable of supporting life, and, after much deliberation, the decision was made to seed only one.'

Mr. Lampard's disclosure confused Tom. If the An'Tsari had chosen to seed only one world, why had he been shown a vision of Mars where life was thriving? It was a dead world now.

Mr. Lampard looked at him nervously. 'When we left, the life we had seeded was beginning to thrive. It seemed perfect, and we were content to return at a later time and observe how life had progressed. But then it happened.'

Tom had expected the old man's words. 'What do you mean - what happened? Surely, it can't have been that bad,' commented Tom. 'We're still here after all. We've managed to survive this far.'

Mr. Lampard's eyes held a deep expression Tom could not fathom. When he spoke, his words were carefully measured. 'Your existence is not the problem. It is your location.'

'Our location?'

The old man nodded. 'You are not where we intended you to be.'

CHAPTER 19

'Why do you persist in talking riddles?' Tom was exasperated. Just when he thought he understood, Mr. Lampard shrouded the truth in another fog of mystery. 'You're holding something back - what aren't you telling me?'

Mr. Lampard considered Tom's words. 'Perhaps it is better that you see.'

'Wait - why did you bring me here? Why this library? What's the significance?'

'There was a turning point during your childhood, a moment where your life took a specific path. It was in that moment that you were destined to be The One. This library represents the moment when that event began.'

'The One?' Tom's *I-don't-believe-this-is-happening-to-me* gesture gave vent to his feelings. He flapped his arms in an expression of frustration and turned away.

The library faded. Seconds later an explosion filled the darkness, an outpouring of light and energy which quickly grew to fill the space around him.

Tom gaped in wonder, his mouth open as the first seconds of the Big Bang unfolded. Staggered by the immensity of creation, he watched as huge swirls of dust and gas cascaded outwards from a single point in space. They twisted and turned upon themselves, drifting together until they began to take on the familiar spiral forms of nebulae and star clusters. They wrapped themselves around one other, colliding in a graceful ballet of light.

A huge spiral galaxy enveloped him, and as it drifted, Tom found himself at its heart. He reached out and the stars of the Milky Way slipped through his fingers.

New stars and planets formed before his eyes. They drifted

past at a greatly accelerated rate until finally the journey slowed, and a single yellow star hung suspended before him. Tom felt the hair on the back of his neck prickle at the sight.

From the glare of the sun a pair of planets circled into view. Their orbits separated them to opposite sides of the parent star, its huge mass hiding one planet from the other.

The first world was blue, oceans covering most of its surface while a single landmass, large and domineering, filled one side of the sphere. He watched as the land mass broke apart, its drift slow and stately. Recognisable land masses formed before his eyes and he watched, mesmerised by the spectacle.

Much of the planet lay shrouded beneath thick cloying smoke, volcanoes belching ash and dust into the atmosphere, but as the clouds swirled he picked out landmasses that would become Africa, Asia and Europe. *Even from the early days it looked like home*, he thought. *Wonderful!*

Earth drifted from view and the second planet rolled along its orbit towards him. It was smaller, its landmass reddish in colour with vast oceans covering most of its surface. A single peak lifted its crown above the thin clouds which scattered its upper atmosphere like a morning haze. Yellowish-red smoke spread into the already discoloured atmosphere as active volcanoes belched a rich soup of heavy chemicals.

Tom understood he was witnessing the early life of two important worlds, but had no concept of their importance, and was unprepared for the vision that came next.

CHAPTER 20

'Both worlds offered a haven for existence, yet Earth was not our first choice.'

'What - you mean Mars was seeded first?' Tom was startled by the admission. 'Why - what happened?'

'At that time Mars orbited closer than Earth, and was a warmer world. Like Earth it had been volcanically active, but it met our needs perfectly. '

Tom understood the logic in Mr. Lampard's words. 'So what happened to all the life you seeded? Where did it go?'

'That is what I need to show you.'

CHAPTER 21

With little volcanic activity the red world had offered safety and stability, and life had flourished. Vegetation spread across the planet's surface, its landmasses washed by salty oceans as the planet's five moons caused its floodplains to rise and fall, and life progressed at an accelerated rate.

It was life with outstanding potential.

*   *   *

Time slowed and the planet crept nearer. Tom found himself within its atmosphere where huge bird-like creatures wheeled gracefully in the warm air. They drifted across the open sky, their wingspans tens of metres wide and their calls mournful in the pink-tinged dawn. Their beaks snapped at flocks of smaller creatures, dividing them like sharks closing in for the kill.

In the distance, delicate domed forms floated gracefully on warm air currents which rose from the lands far below. As thin as tissue paper, their skins captured the slightest rising currents as they drifted around the skies of the planet. Their purpose unknown, the floaters had once existed only in the skies of early Mars. They were a life form which had not evolved on Earth, and they fascinated Tom.

Descending towards the grass covered plains, thousands of years passed in an instant. Herds of cattle lumbered across the rolling hilltops, their shaggy coated bodies and heavy feet raising red dust high into the sky. They grazed on the large bushes that dotted the landscape, the orange flowers that sprouted from their leafy tips a source of food hungrily sought out by the cattle.

'This is fantastic!' exclaimed Tom, his excitement almost breathless. 'Pterodactyls, cattle - it's so like Earth.'

'And it should have evolved further, only something

unexpected happened.'

When Tom next opened his eyes he was under a beautiful blue sky. Trees taller than those of Earth reached high above while waves lapped peacefully against his feet. Birdsong drew his attention, its Earth-like quality relaxing and disarming, yet subtly different.

A small disc shone brightly overhead, and five other points of light chased each other towards the horizon. Tom realised they were moons, and he watched in awe as the first drifted towards a range of low hills. A final flare of sunlight reflected from it before the moon vanished from sight. *The Mars I'm standing on now is in a different orbit*, thought Tom. *It's warm and it has life.*

'What happened here?' He almost spat the question at Mr. Lampard, but the old man merely pointed towards the heavens.

The sky was suddenly filled with a dark seething mass. Tendrils of fire raked across half the sky as the asteroid ploughed through the lower atmosphere. Tom felt the air in his lungs quickly heat up and he gasped for breath.

A torrent of wind thrust him backwards, its power forcing him into the water. Waves whipped around his legs, their power pulling him under, and his mouth filled with gritty sand and gagging water. Unable to pull himself above the surface, Tom felt life ebb from his body for a second time, and as it did, Mr. Lampard spoke.

The voice was clear inside his mind. *The asteroid was so large, its passage through the atmosphere so ferocious, that it set the atmosphere alight. It ripped oxygen from the planet by the power of its passing, burning it and setting the landscape alight. Mars reeled under the assault, but worse was to come.*

The nucleus of the asteroid was composed of heavy metals with strong magnetic properties. It began to break up, and as fragments spiralled away they wrenched at the iron core of the planet. Both planet and asteroid moved as one, until finally the planet was left to drift, but the damage had been done.

The asteroid destroyed all that we had achieved. The atmosphere leaked away to space and the pressure around the planet lessened; the oceans vanished and all life that had not been incinerated by fire, or suffocated by the escaping atmosphere, was extinguished.

By the time the planet had settled into a colder orbit, all evidence of life had been eradicated. The planet died.

We were shocked. Never before had such a disaster threatened to destroy our existence, and for a time we did not know what to do.

Mr. Lampard fell silent as water flooded Tom's lungs. Suffocation dragged him towards oblivion and his body gave in to the effects of drowning.

As consciousness slipped away, Mr. Lampard's final words resonated clearly inside his head: *Everything you need is here. You will know what to do.*

CHAPTER 22

The Deep Space Observation Platform was in orbit to aide the search for extra-terrestrial intelligence. Dubbed *Sagan's Eye* after scientist and astronomer Carl Sagan, the Platform was NASA's eyes on the distant universe. It was the most complex and sensitive optical instrument in existence, and, when the storm hit, the decision was made to reposition the Platform to work alongside the Mars Mission Telescope.

Chief Planetary Scientist Adam Benedict knew Mars better than he knew his own family, or so everyone said. There was nothing about his favourite planet that fazed him, so when his computer flagged orbital errors, Benedict was puzzled. He cross-checked his data, but was unable to believe the figures before him. They showed Mars falling out of orbit, yet he knew it was impossible. He pursed his lips and studied the data; he knew there must be a simple explanation, but was at a loss to understand what it could be.

A new set of figures caught his eye and he frowned. 'Aw, come on. What are you playing at..?'

'Problem?' Sarah Rayburn leant over from her adjoining desk and studied Benedict's screen.

'Messy data. According to this, Mars is shifting orbit.' He snorted in disbelief. 'Like we all know *that's* gonna happen!'

Sarah Rayburn's smile creased the corners of her eyes and made them sparkle. Benedict cast his eye over her screen. 'I guess it's just the storm playing screwball with everything. What about you?' He leant in closer. 'Is your data off?'

'Actually, no. The numbers are where they should be.'

Adam's smile faltered. 'But your data is from the same source as mine. You're measuring...'

'Atmospheric pressure; temperature; wind speed...'

'But it's from the Mars telescope, right? You're...'

'No, *Sagan's Eye*. I switched over a couple of hours ago, but...wait a minute, I'm registering a drop off - ' She refreshed her data but it continued to trail off as she watched.

Alarms sounded as computers all around the control room lost data lock and Benedict's headset quickly filled with confused chatter. The room fell into chaos.

A single voice cut through the clamour, and the room hushed. Flight Director Jack Tyreman commanded respect. When he spoke, everyone listened.

'Right, people, I want an analysis of what just happened: I want to know the situation prior to our loss of data - if anyone had any rogue numbers or an indication that something was amiss - and any problems reported by outside agencies. In short, I want anything and everything, including off-the-wall ideas you might have. Confer with your department heads and pull it all together quickly. We have six people up there depending on us and we need to know what just happened. I want that data ASAP. Let's move it, people.'

Adam keyed his mike. 'Flight, this is Planetary Science.'

'Go ahead.'

'Just before our loss of data my orbital figures were off.'

'What do you mean, they were off?' The Flight Director wasn't in the mood for guessing games. 'I need specifics.'

'They were telling me Mars wasn't there.'

'Wasn't there?'

Adam continued. 'Has the Mars Telescope had an alignment failure? What about the Deep Space Telescope? Has there been a change to either telescope's orbit?'

'That would explain a lot. Let me check.'

Adam's earpiece clicked as the connection was broken. He looked at Sarah Rayburn. 'Either the downlink to Mission Control has gone, the Mars Telescope has moved, or...' He didn't finish his sentence. The possibility was simply too preposterous even to contemplate.

CHAPTER 23

Phobos fell from orbit with a hammer blow's force. The small moon had circled Mars for over four billion years, captured by the red planet as it wandered through the early solar system. Now, rushing towards the planet at over thirty thousand kilometres an hour, Phobos crushed the thin atmosphere beneath it into a solid wall of destruction. The steely barrier acted like a blunt instrument, gouging dust and rock from the ground ahead, creating a seething bubble of dust, rock and superheated water vapour as the ice within it vaporised.

The falling moon exploded. Its disintegration ripped the surface apart with a force greater than the combined nuclear warheads of planet Earth.

Instantly much of the rocky crust vaporised, but the frozen sub-layers fared better. Pulverised, blasted high into the Martian atmosphere, they would rain a hail of destruction on a planet-wide scale, the falling rocks pummelling the planet with a barrage of devastation.

Vast subterranean lakes, frozen for hundreds of millions of years and long hidden from the ravages of solar radiation, were suddenly exposed to intense heat. Their frozen water was vaporised, releasing precious hydrogen and oxygen into the atmosphere as the moon's frozen heart vanished.

The impact vibrated deep into the core and the planet rang like a great iron bell. Stores of ice, deep beneath the surface, vaporised instantly, exerting intense pressure on already straining fault lines, and Mars rumbled as dormant volcanic activity stirred. Gaping rents spread quickly outwards from the point of impact, and for the first time in ten million years, Mars awoke.

CHAPTER 24

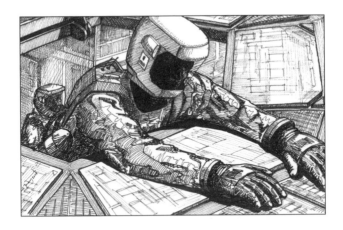

The atmosphere inside the shelter was heavy. Buried beneath the surface of the planet, shielded by heavy insulation and tons of Martian rock, the crew knew they were safe.

Jack awoke slowly and stared at the hatch above them for what seemed like the thousandth time. He had counted and recounted the rivets in the past six days and found himself doing it again. Irritated, he sat up and stretched his arms until his shoulders clicked, the stiffness in his back caused by a lack of exercise and the confines of an uncomfortable bunk.

He froze mid-stretch as he sensed something was different. It took a moment before he realised what it was: the wind had died.

'Hey, guys. Wake up!' He whistled. Frank stirred and raised his head.

Jack pointed upwards and gestured with his eyes. 'Listen.'

Irina rolled over, her face red where it had been cushioned against her arm. A line of saliva dribbled from the corner of her mouth and she wiped it away with the back of her hand.

'The wind's stopped. Everything's quiet - listen.' For several seconds the only sound was the steady background hiss of the air recyclers and their own breathing. It was a sound they hadn't heard clearly for nearly a week.

Jack stepped over to a console and checked the readouts. 'Wind's down to twelve km/h.' He turned and smiled. 'A typical Martian day. Looks good.' He stepped away, his expression determined. 'I'm going top-side.'

Frank and Irina glanced at each other: Commander or not, Jack could still be vetoed out of a course of action if other crew members considered it too dangerous. But they needed to know the damage the storm had wreaked above them.

Frank opened a locker and pulled out three lightweight emergency pressure suits; they were designed to keep an astronaut alive for a short time, but would offer little protection against radiation. He passed them around and stripped the seals open on his own suit before kicking off his shoes. 'If the station has been holed, these will at least allow us to reach the HardSuits and begin repairs.' His tone didn't sound too hopeful.

Irina agreed. 'If there's anything left to repair.' She instantly wished she hadn't spoken. There was a strong probability her words could be the truth.

Three suited figures faced each other. Once their visors were lowered they would be safe against any loss of pressure beyond the hatch, but their whole world may be confined to the limited oxygen supply each suit carried. *Thirty minutes*, thought Frank. *That's all we may have left*. He patted his oxygen cylinder subconsciously, as though it were his last grasp on the real world

'Are you sure you guys want to come?' Jack spoke calmly. 'If the radiation is still high out there, we won't have much of a chance. Once we step through that hatch there's no going back.'

Irina switched on her helmet mike and locked her visor; her action was stronger than anything she could have voiced.

'What about you?' Jack turned to Frank and saw the

Frenchman's visor already closed. He knew he had his full commitment; it was no less than he expected.

Jack nodded, placed a hand on the arm of each suited figure, and climbed the ladder. He paused to lock his own visor and then slid the first two locking clamps into the OPEN position with a heavy *clunk*. He reached for the final latch.

Jack had no idea what would happen once he slid the latch open; if the station had been holed there could very well be no atmosphere above, and the difference in pressure would rip the hatch open.

But the station could be fully intact, the atmosphere breathable. It may be as they had left it almost a week ago, but they had no way of knowing.

Why didn't the designers think to fit extraction pumps in here? he thought. We could lose our oxygen supply as soon as the hatch opens.

Jack looked down at the strained faces. 'You guys ready?'

'Do it.' Frank's voice was determined, his expression grim.

Gripping the handle tightly, Jack slid it all the way over and quickly let go: he didn't want to lose his arm if the hatch suddenly ripped open, but it remained closed. It didn't even judder.

The silence surprised them all, and Jack tentatively levered the hatch open before shining his helmet lamps into the darkness above. He clambered up, Irina and Frank close behind, and they paused as if entering a new world for the first time.

The world they found was unexpected; a discarded jacket hung on a workstation chair, a half filled glass of water on a worktop and the jumbled innards of the computer Jack had been repairing were just as they had left them a week ago. The only difference appeared to be a litter of manuals scattered across the deck plates, disturbed by some errant force. Otherwise, everything appeared much as they remembered.

Jack turned a slow circle and played his helmet lamps across the ceiling. With no tell tale trickles of red dust from the world outside, the shelter appeared to be intact.

He stepped towards a workstation and flicked a series of

switches, but the monitor remained blank. He tried another. 'Main frame is down.' He opened a panel on the wrist of his suit and set its computer to work, the readings appearing quickly on its digital screen. 'Radiation levels are a touch high, but liveable. That's a good start.'

He turned to Frank. 'We need power restored as a priority, then I need a full systems check before we step foot out of this room; air recyclers, water, communications - I want to know exactly what state we're in. I also want a summary of conditions outside. We need to know what's going on.'

He turned to Irina but she was already sorting through the contents of a storage locker. She pulled out a number of hand-held devices and docked them into waiting terminals.

Data presented itself on the small screen in her hand as she moved between devices. Satisfied with the upload, she moved on and repeated the exercise. Immersed in the data, she was oblivious to the activity around her.

Kneeling by a deck panel, Frank heaved it open. He ducked his upper body inside the opening, grunted with the effort, and wormed his way deeper. Lights suddenly sprang to life around the room and monitors flickered as the station's computers came online. It was as though a great beast had awakened from its winter sleep and had begun flexing its muscles. Jack smiled.

Things didn't seem so bad after all.

Initial reports were good. Power was back online, level one was intact and both heaters and air recyclers were working at full capacity. Whether or not the rest of the station was in a similar condition was unknown, but for the moment they had oxygen, water and heat.

'So, what's the score outside?' Jack watched intently as Irina studied her handheld device.

'I'm receiving an update now.' She waited a few seconds for it to complete uploading. 'Okay. Wind speed is from the north and within safe limits, but the atmosphere has...' She paused as she double checked her data. Her expression showed confusion. 'This is incredible - the atmosphere currently has an 11.73 percent trace of oxygen, and a 14.36 percent trace of water.' She shook her head. 'These reading can't be right – there's no way the atmosphere could have thickened so much while we've been below.'

Jack took the device and refreshed the data, his own face belying his surprise. 'According to this, readings are continuing to climb: water vapour has increased again, look.' He passed the device back to Irina. 'If those figures are right – '

Irina worked quickly. 'The figures are changing as we speak. Temperatures have gone up twelve degrees in the past sixty minutes and the atmosphere is continuing to thicken.' She sighed in exasperation. 'Whatever's happening, Mars has undergone extreme warming. Whether or not it's global, I can't tell.'

Frank perched on the edge of a workstation and dropped his helmet onto a seat. Jack and Irina had removed theirs earlier when Frank had been inside the access panel. 'Mars hasn't had a temperature rise like that for what - billions of years? Your readings must be wrong; the radiation must have screwed the sensors. Have you reset them?'

'Twice, and the results are the same. If this is right, then Mars is warming up, and fast.'

'And the water...'

'...can only be from the poles.' She waved her hands in supplication. 'Your guess is as good as mine, but if water is being released from the poles then it's very likely the source of oxygen. I would guess the storm has triggered some kind of chemical reaction: let's face it, it's not that difficult to extract oxygen from water.'

She tapped at her device. 'And look at this.' She held it out to Frank. 'While we were in the shelter radiation levels went through the roof. They reached over a thousand times our annual limit.'

Frank folded his arms as he studied the screen. 'Okay, but

what do we do now? What's our course of action? We can't leave the others out there - we owe it to them to bring them home...' He didn't finish his sentence, but with such high radiation readings he knew there would be very little chance that Tom, Naina and Tiny had survived.

Irina put her hand on the nape of his neck and massaged the muscles there. She shared his tension. They all did. 'I know, but we can't do anything until we've checked the station and restored communications. That's our priority now.' She looked at Jack for agreement. 'It's what they would do.'

Jack nodded. 'We're alive and need to stay that way. Houston will be looking for some kind of a signal, something to indicate we've survived. It's up to us to give it to them. Once we're secure we can start thinking about recovery.' He struggled to find a better way to explain it. 'I know it's hard, but that's the way it has to be.'

Frank nodded, his movements slow as he mulled over what he knew to be right. Jack's words made sense.

The Commander picked up his helmet. 'It looks as though the storm is over, at least for now. Come on, let's try the next level.'

CHAPTER 25

A blast of air thrust the hatch inwards and Frank forced it shut. He braced it with his shoulder and locked it again.

'We're holed,' he said. 'If we open the hatch our atmosphere will escape.'

'Wait a minute...' Irina indicated the direction of air movement. 'The hatch was forced inwards – that means the pressure beyond the hatch must be greater than within.'

Jack removed his glove and placed his hand against the hatch as though trying to gauge the atmosphere on the other side. 'The outer pressure was trying to equalise itself with the lower pressure in here.' He smiled. 'That means we're okay.'

Frank moved away and Jack pulled the lever back. It chattered as the warm air rushed in, the disturbance only lasting for a few seconds. When it ceased, he opened the hatch all the way and found a scene much the same as when they first left the shelter.

'This section of the station has a higher roof,' Jack said. He checked the readout on his suit computer and found it more than forty degrees warmer. 'The storm's radiation must have heated the air and the station's insulation maintained the temperature. With the power out the extraction fans weren't able to cut in and cool it down.'

'So the air expanded.' Frank laughed at himself.

Irina clapped him on the back. 'Some scientist, huh?' Frank smiled.

The room they stepped into was undisturbed. 'If we carry on at this rate we'll be in good shape,' said Jack. He looked around. Had fate left them a guiding hand? Everything seemed to point that way, but Irina's words brought him back with a cold jolt.

'Remember the observation blister.' Her face showed panic as the bubble disintegrated again in her head, the sound haunting her once more.

Frank studied her expression. 'Let's hope that's all we've lost.'

Jack's voice sounded in both their earpieces. 'Okay, let's try level three,' he said. 'You guys ready?'

* * *

Tiny struggled to keep to his feet as another tremor shuddered through the cave.

Naina steadied herself as she waited for the next judder. 'How long is this going to carry on?' Her computer beeped once again and a warning symbol flashed across her visor. Data scrolled beneath it, the numbers increasing as she watched. They changed so rapidly that she couldn't believe what she was seeing. Her body shook with the force of another tremor. 'The atmosphere - it's thickening: water vapour, carbon dioxide, nitrogen, oxygen, they're all in abundance!' Even in the midst of the Marsquake she took vital seconds to contemplate what she was seeing. 'It's incredible!'

'How?' Tiny's mouth was stretched thin with anxiety.

'Something's happened: the storm, the thickening of the atmosphere, the quake. Something big has happened.'

Tiny struggled to focus and realised it wasn't a problem with his eyes. Everything swirled in a misty redness as dust billowed in the beams of his helmet lamps. The atmosphere outside whipped itself into another wild flurry and fresh clouds blew in through the cave entrance.

Naina steadied herself long enough to study the data. 'But that's impossible - there isn't enough gas in the atmosphere to create that kind of pressure. It would need the release of vast quantities of trapped oxygen from the poles to begin thickening the atmosphere, and even then...'

As the words left her lips Naina doubted they could be true, but the evidence was compelling. They could see it happening before their eyes.

'But why the quake? Why the storm?' Tiny's lips cracked as he spoke, and he tasted blood.

'We've recorded planet-wide storms before, but never on this scale. The temperature increases...' She was lost for words. 'There must have been an impact of some kind.' The quake eased for a moment but she barely noticed. 'Comet strike; asteroid impact.' Her mind ran through the possibilities. 'That could account for some of the water vapour, but...'

Tiny's response was drowned by the grinding of rock. Chunks of ice scattered across the floor of the cave as the ceiling buckled, a small landslip bringing down the roof somewhere in the depths of the cave. A second and third tremor followed, each time showering the floor with fresh debris and Naina shouted her alarm as the cave roof visibly shifted. 'We've got to get out of here! The roof is coming in!'

She grabbed Tiny and dragged him away from the cave wall. Her helmet lamps illuminated the narrow depths as she turned, and her beams cut through the murky atmosphere. She froze.

The depths of the cave churned and bubbled as it moved. Great hunks of ice were thrust forwards, smaller pieces skittering around her feet as the ice plug which had sealed the depths of the cave finally gave way. A reddish-brown outpouring surged forwards, eating up their only shelter against the storm outside.

Naina felt a shot of adrenaline, her flesh running hot and cold at the same time, and her heart thumped so hard in her chest it felt as though it may burst out through her HardSuit. 'This is not good,' she said. She backed away from the advancing wall of ice and turned towards Tiny, prepared to move out into the storm and take her chances. She grabbed him by the arm and turned towards the opening when another figure stepped into view.

It was Tom.

CHAPTER 26

The situation inside *Foothold* station was better than they could have wished, the only major damage being the loss of the observation blister, but the fate of Tom, Naina and Tiny weighed heavily on the remaining crew members' minds.

'We know approximately where they were when the storm hit, but that doesn't mean anything. They could have been forced to run or hole up somewhere.' Jack tried to sound positive.

Frank found it difficult to accept. 'We can't just sit here and presume they're dead,' he said. 'For all we know they could be out there hanging onto life, half expecting us to come riding over the hill like bold Gendarmes. We have to do something!'

'We're not leaving them out there.' Jack was struggling to keep Frank under control: his behaviour was erratic and it concerned the Commander. He tried a different approach. 'Look, we're going out there – soon - but our first priority is to ourselves. Until we understand more about what's happened it makes sense to stay here. We need to ensure we have a good grasp of the situation: we don't want any nasty surprises once we're beyond that airlock.'

'Jack's right.' Irina put her arm around Frank's shoulders and guided him gently towards a seat. 'Personal safety is number one. You know the mission protocols.' They sat down and Irina squeezed his hand gently.

Jack paced the floor as he spoke. 'Okay, we need as much background as possible before we decide on our next move.' His manner was matter-of-fact. 'What do we know?'

Irina consulted her handheld device. 'Well, our readings tell us that atmospheric temperatures are on the rise: either that or our sensors are out of alignment, although I've reset everything.

She shrugged. 'But if the main sensor grid was fried by the storm, we'll have no way of knowing what the truth is.' She squeezed Frank's hand once more and he smiled, then moved to access more data. 'According to this, wind speeds have gusted in excess of one thousand kilometres per hour, and visibility is seriously impaired by the quantities of dust suspended in the atmosphere. That will also affect sending and receiving radio transmissions.'

'So what you're saying is we're deaf, dumb and blind,' Jack concluded.

Irina nodded. 'For the moment, yes, but it should start to improve as long as the wind doesn't pick up again.'

Jack pondered the situation. 'What about the Guardians?' He directed the question at Frank.

'Uh?' The Frenchman stumbled before organising his thoughts on the technical aspects of the situation. 'Right - the hi-gain antenna seems undamaged and is transmitting on all frequencies, but for some reason the Guardians are out of contact. With us always remaining in direct line-of-sight with Guardian 1 the signal should be getting through. Except it isn't.'

Guardian 1 maintained its orbit directly above *Foothold* station, the planet's 24.6 hour rotation ensuring that as the station turned away from Earth, one of the remaining two satellites moved into a communications position with Earth: *Foothold* was never out of contact with Mission Control.

'Could it be that the solar flare has knocked out the Guardian's systems? I know they're heavily shielded against solar radiation, but that storm was off the scale.' Jack's proposal was plausible.

'It's more than likely.' Frank had tried a number of tests, but had no way of knowing that Guardian 1 lay smashed across the surface of the planet while Guardians 2 and 3 spun uncontrollably in space. 'We just don't know.'

'Okay.' Jack pulled a seat from under the workstation and sat down. 'So we don't have any real-time data to go on, other than what we can gather from here, and no person-to-person communication with anyone outside this station. The only thing we do know is where EV-2 was heading before the storm hit.' He looked at his friends, castaways on a world more than four million kilometres from home, and found himself smiling at the memory of an old movie he'd once seen – *Robinson Crusoe on Mars*. He laughed at the irony: who'd have ever thought it would actually come true?

'What's funny?' Irina looked at him quizzically.

'Nothing. Just a random thought. Come on,' he said as he stood up, a smile of absurdity crossing his lips. 'Let's check out the rest of the station.'

* * *

They felt the tremor before they heard it, and within seconds the peaceful world they had known for so long suddenly became an angry, violent monster.

The station tilted upwards, the floor replaced by a wall. In the low gravity Jack was thrown in slow motion. He reached out to steady himself but his arms grasped at empty space.

Electrical explosions filled the air as the power system gave in under the strain, workstations sparking in protest as the station twisted unexpectedly.

Tortured beyond all limits, the bulkheads began to crack. The sudden darkness was filled with terrifying sounds and everything shifted violently once more. Jack lost all sense of position as he tumbled, his fall arrested by something hard; it dug into his ribs like a knife and thrust the air from his lungs by the force of the impact.

Heat splashed across his right hand as the insulating wall of water, which protected Foothold from the outside temperatures, was breached. It was the last thing he had expected to feel, but its implications were immense.

He cast his helmet lamps around as he searched frantically for his glove. If their atmosphere escaped before he sealed his glove into place, his suit would depressurise. The prospect terrified him.

A flash of white. There. His glove lay about three metres away, but no matter how hard he struggled, the shifting station prevented him from moving any closer.

With unsteady legs he launched himself towards the glove once more, but his trajectory was altered as the station shifted again, another tremor striking hard and rattling everything around him. His arms flailed and he missed.

A loud crack split the air, followed by an aggressive hissing. It was the sound all spacers dreaded – the sound of escaping air. His heart thumped so heavily he felt it in his temples. He *had* to reach his glove, but his years of training seemed unable to help.

He knew he was only seconds away from death, but didn't want to die here.

Not this way.

Not now.

A voice filled his ears but the words didn't register, his own panic blocking everything. The words were repeated and Jack felt himself held by strong hands. He looked up as something was thrust at him.

He felt his wrist being grabbed, something tugged over his hand and the double clamps snapped shut. A familiar fabric enclosed his fingers and he looked up into Frank's face.

'Hey, Boss. Thought you needed a hand.'

Jack gripped his friend by the shoulder and squeezed. Tears filled his eyes, his voice thick. 'Thanks, Frank. Really, thanks.'

'No problem.'

The station moved again. The sound of hissing increased as the hole in the station wall widened.

Frank flashed his lamps into the darkness, his beams cutting a white swathe through the misty atmosphere. The two men held onto each other for support while they searched for Irina, and in the glare of his lamps, they saw something fall.

She had no time to shield herself as the chair's spear-like leg struck her visor. Web-like cracks instantly distorted her vision and she let out a yell.

Irina fumbled for a pouch on her leg, but Frank was quicker.

He brushed away her hands and pulled an adhesive pad from her emergency kit, slapping it across her visor to seal the damage instantly. The visor held, but the measure was only temporary. 'That should hold for a while,' said Frank, 'but we need to get moving.' He was breathless, his movements erratic. The station rocked again and the floor tilted further.

'We have to get out of here - where's the airlock?' Jack's voice was urgent.

Frank made a decision and reached for Irina. 'Here - grab my hand!' They clasped fingers in the darkness and he pulled her upright. 'This way!'

They clambered onto the remains of a workstation and used it to climb towards a tear in the station wall, its metal and plastic structure torn like wet cardboard. The supporting framework was visible in the brightness of his lights and Frank knew they would need to take care stepping through; the tiniest tear would cause their suits to depressurise.

The ground twisted again beneath the station and Frank and Irina clawed for support against the workstation before climbing higher. By the time they reached the station wall, Jack was through. He reached out to Irina.

'Come on. Take my hand. Hurry!' He glanced at Frank. 'Watch that support, Frank. Watch it doesn't catch her shoulder.'

Frank placed one hand over a sharp edge and shielded Irina's suit as she passed through. 'Go on, you're doing fine.' He eased her shoulders through the gap, and then followed. He had to bend his knees slightly to worm his way through, and followed up a low incline.

Scrambling across shifting ground, they rounded the station and moved towards EV-1. The vehicle's wheels were buried axle deep in rock and dust and it stood at a rakish angle. The ground shook again and it settled deeper into the ground as they approached.

Jack hit the airlock keypad. 'C'mon, c'mon, c'mon!' he shouted impatiently as the airlock cycled open. Time dragged relentlessly, but finally they clambered through and the hatch slid closed behind them. Jack pressed the *Emergency Pressurise* button and oxygen blasted into the airlock. The dust they had tramped in whipped up like a thick fog, and as the inner hatch slid open they staggered into the crew compartment amid a red haze.

Frank braced his feet and lowered Irina into a waiting couch. He strapped her in, slid into the seat opposite and buckled his own lap belt before stripping off his gloves and reaching out towards her. He brushed her trembling fingers away from her helmet latches and she gave in without complaint.

The helmet came away with a hiss of compressed air. He dropped it onto the deck so Irina couldn't see its cracked visor and pulled her gloves off. Her hands shook badly and she gripped his fingers tightly, her fingers cold with shock. She needed physical contact more than anything; her smile tight and forced, her voice small. 'Thanks.'

The engines whined to life. 'You guys strapped in?' yelled Jack. 'This is gonna be rough!'

The engines strained and the vehicle lurched. Sunken wheels dragged themselves from the rock and dust, then lost their grip and the vehicle slumped back.

Jack raced the engines once more and held them at full throttle until, with a shudder, the vehicle pulled away. 'Coming around.' He steered the vehicle in a large arc away from the station and opened the throttles to maximum. The engines screamed at the demand but performed flawlessly, their tyres gripping bare bedrock and thrusting them forward with increasing speed.

Behind them *Foothold* station lay cracked and broken. The huge conical mound of the habitation module and spoke-like science modules lay half buried, their insides exposed as the ground rippled and shifted. Cracks raced through the bedrock as the ground splintered, and the station modules disappeared one by one. Plumes of oxygen vented in billowing clouds and a wall of water sprayed upwards as the station's tanks ruptured. The liquid froze instantly and was whipped away by the swirling winds in a fountain of pure white snow against a backdrop of red.

It was as if the planet were mocking them - extinguishing their only hope of survival.

Jack switched on the disaster beacon, its flash on the console a sense of security amid the chaos, and headed away from the station at full speed. The vehicle rode rough-shod over the uneven ground, but there was one last hope, if only they could get to it.

They circled the remains of the station and headed east towards the plains where the lander stood. If the ground had shifted beneath it, there was every probability it would be nothing more than a useless heap of twisted metal and plastic, but there was still a possibility it would be intact.

If it were intact, they could try and reach orbit, rendezvous with the rest of the ship and break orbit. They wouldn't be in a position to return to Earth - the orbits of Mars and Earth were not aligned to allow them to return home for another four months – but at least they would be able to leave this tortured world behind. They could orbit the sun and await rescue, or orbit the sun and wait to die. They would only know once they left orbit.

But what about Tom, Naina and Tiny? They couldn't leave without knowing if the other members of the crew were dead or alive, and Jack knew they had one other task to accomplish before they ignited the landers' engines and raced into orbit.

Jack piloted the vehicle towards the landing co-ordinates, his mind made up. Once there they would power up the landers' systems and gain enough height to attempt a 'hop' - they would fly across the surface and touch down close to Team 2's last known position.

It's a slim chance, thought Jack, *but it's all we have.*

And then the landing site came into view.

CHAPTER 27

'This is impossible - you're dead!' Naina's voice shook as she stared at Tom. 'Your visor's broken – you can't possibly breathe. There's nothing here *to* breathe!'

Words filled Naina's head, their tone soothing. She sensed rather than heard them.

We must go now. Come with me.

Naina didn't move until urged forward by a hand against her back. 'I don't care if he's dead or not,' grumbled Tiny. 'If we stay here, we will be! Let's do what the man says.'

Naina gave in to the demand. Another tremor shook the cave and she fell. She hit the rocky incline sideways and rolled, her feet breaking her descent.

Tom stepped confidently ahead, his outstretched hand something she didn't really want to touch. Tiny addressed Tom as he lifted Naina back onto her feet. 'It's okay, buddy, I've got her. Just let the lady be.' His words were clipped and his voice trembled. He didn't understand what was going on, the pain of losing his friend still fresh. But now Tom stood before him. The situation was impossible to comprehend.

Tom's voice sounded again. *I understand your surprise, but do not be afraid: I am still your friend.*

Rocks cracked and splintered as new tremors caused the sides of the ravine to disintegrate above them. A large rupture ejected a curtain of water high into the sky, and within seconds all three figures were ankle deep in sludge as the ice and water deepened.

A deep rumble shook the ground, and Tiny and Naina struggled to keep their feet. Tom held out a hand again, his words clear in Tiny's ears. *We must leave here.*

Another tremor shook the ground and an ice plug above them gave way. A wave of dirty ice-water cascaded into the riverbed and Naina went rigid as she realised it had emerged from the cave in which they had sheltered. Splintered rocks and dust tumbled as the ice moved quickly in Mars' low gravity, and the ancient riverbed filled with flowing water-ice within seconds. Boulders were scraped from the towering walls in great landslips, and then, with a suddenness that winded all three astronauts, the bed of the ravine rose.

It arced upwards with devastating force. The walls crumbled in slow motion and fell forward; avalanches of rock descended in a slow motion wall of destruction, and struck the raging water-ice below.

A plume of ice-liquid was thrown up, its mass peppered with boulders and smaller rocks that hung suspended high above, until at last it began its slow fall back towards the surface.

And as it fell, Tiny reached out. He took hold of both Naina and Tom's hands, and waited for the end.

CHAPTER 28

Everything rattled.

If it weren't for the seatbelt, Irina felt sure her body would fall apart. It was worse than the bone-shaking, tooth-rattling stresses of lift off.

That had been an experience she would never forget; the boosters had ignited beneath her, hurling the rocket into orbit at more than forty thousand kilometres per hour. *Spam in a can*, Chuck Yeager had called it, and the Mercury astronauts should know: their lift-offs had been much more aggressive than those experienced by today's spacers, but Irina's had been bad enough.

Lying back in the headrest she braced her neck muscles. If she ended up with a stiff neck, at least she would know she was still alive. Right now she half expected to be dead within the next thirty seconds, and every second beyond that seemed like a miracle.

The EV rocked as the ground beneath it shifted, each tremor riding on the back of another. Irina had given up screaming in terror, every ounce of strength now directed to holding herself together. No matter how much physical training or emotional conditioning NASA had given her, nothing could have prepared her for this.

Frank had moved up to the cockpit once he was able to stand. He shouted over the coarse rumblings which split the air of the cabin and fought with Jack to keep the vehicle level. Ahead, silhouetted against the dust-filled sky, a squat lander stood precariously on four spindly legs. Designed around the Apollo Moon landing craft, it was a proud design harking back to the glory days of NASA's race to the Moon. Constructed with state of the art materials and crammed with computer systems not even dreamt about ten years ago, the lander was their only hope of escape.

The vibrations increased and two of the lander's legs collapsed. The module settled onto its side, the descent-stage housing, engine bell and fuel tanks crushed against the hard rock of the planet, and its liquid hydrogen fuel leaked away into the thickening atmosphere.

Another tremor shook the planet and the hard ground beneath the lander opened up. The vehicle pitched to one side, its structure twisted and mangled beyond recognition, and, in a final spray of dust and rock, sunk into the crevasse and vanished.

The hilltop gave an unexpected lurch and a depression raced towards the EV. Frank made a hurried decision. 'That way! That way! The ground is less broken! If we can get away from...'

The vehicle bucked and Jack spoke sharply as the ground beneath them dropped. 'The wheels won't co-operate!' He fought with the controls and revved the engines as he battled the vehicle towards a shallow incline. The motors raced and plumes of rocky shale sprayed from beneath the wheels as the vehicle lurched. It righted itself and ploughed on.

As they crested the hill, a plume of thick smoke billowed high into the atmosphere. Below it, a volcano spewed ash and dust high into the Martian sky, but despite the distance, the volcano's effect was overpowering.

'Oh, my - look at that!' Jack glanced up at Frank's

exclamation. He stared open mouthed, then shouted back to Irina.

'Hey, Irina. You gotta see this!' He punched a button on the panel before him and the monitors came to life in the crew compartment. 'This is incredible!'

The cameras zoomed in and Frank let out another cry. 'Now that's something I *didn't* expect to see!'

Irina felt her neck muscles creak as she turned towards the screens. She sat up and leaned forward, her discomfort momentarily forgotten as she stared at the monitor.

'That's Olympus Mons – it's active!' Her head reeled under the shock of so vivid an image. 'But if Olympus is active, then the whole mantle is probably active as well.' She wet her lips. 'We're sitting on a volcanic bomb!'

Irina shuddered at the thought of the planet's internal heat forcing its way out through the thin crust. Mars had a long history of volcanic activity, but because the planet did not have the same shifting plate tectonics as Earth, it had little recent volcanic activity to show. On Earth, volcanoes erupted and then fell dormant as the flow of lava was blocked, but here whole areas of the Martian crust would be subject to intense heating and pressure.

The pressures involved were immense, the forces deep underground powerful enough to change the surface of the entire planet. Billions of years ago the Tharsis region had been created when an area the size of North America had buckled under intense strain; the crust had stretched and cracked, forming the great rift valley now known as the Valles Marineris.

But now, riding inside a tin can across a cracked and crumbling volcanic landscape, Irina felt vulnerable. She tried to dismiss the thoughts, but her heart hammered with every tremor.

Unbuckling herself, she pulled her adrenaline-soaked body into the empty seat behind Jack as a loud report vibrated up from the surface below. Another followed, and the vehicle shuddered and creaked.

'What was *that?*' Jack kept his eyes on the route before him as Frank glanced anxiously around.

'I can't see anything.' He paused. 'Oh, no! It can't be!'

Irina thrust her head into his window, and her blood ran icily cold. Her heart thudded in her chest and she sagged where she stood, her grip on Frank's chair the only thing which prevented her from falling as her legs failed.

A crumbling fault line raced towards them, and the ground dropped away to reveal a deep chasm. Frank shouted in alarm and Jack glanced around. The sight made his guts wrench.

'That way! That way! Quick!' Frank lunged at the wheel and the two men forced the vehicle into a turn. It lurched drunkenly, its suspension rolling with the sudden change of direction, before struggling onto a new course. The EV's wheels skidded on the lose bedrock and finally caught, but it wasn't enough.

Even as the vehicle turned, even as its wheels bit into the rocky surface, the ground opened up around them. A gaping crevasse tens of metres wide grumbled and shook as the landscape was torn open like paper. Bedrock fell away in its ravening path; the vibration terrifying, the noise thunderous, even in the thin atmosphere.

With the slow motion horror of a nightmare, the surface of the planet slipped from beneath the vehicle's wheels, and the EV began to fall.

The EV had been designed with three axles, each turning a pair of large treaded wheels. Should the need arise, the vehicle could balance its weight on two axles, as long as it remained within forty degrees of horizontal. It could also climb much steeper inclines than on Earth, but with the torturous vibrations shaking the vehicle, it had reached its limits.

As the plateau fell away the rear wheels tore desperately at empty space. The onboard computers registered that axle three was no longer in contact with solid ground and increased output to the remaining axles. They bit into the surface with renewed vigour, and a screaming whine penetrated the cabin like a shriek of desperation. The engines struggled to pull the vehicle towards solid ground and safety, but it was not to be.

The EV's own weight dragged it backwards towards the crumbling edge of the crevasse, and the edge beneath it began to break up. Rock fell away slowly and the centre axle slipped, its grip reduced as the vehicle teetered around its centre of gravity. With a sickening lurch the EV hung by its front wheels. Its under-body gouged at the rocky edge in a last desperate attempt at survival, but as all hope vanished, EV-1 slipped over the edge and into the darkness below.

CHAPTER 29

Empty HardSuits stood like over-sized mannequins, their lights and visors dark. Tiny knew he was in the maintenance bay.

Fresh oxygen flooded his lungs and Tiny realised he was connected to the EV's life support systems. A sharp pain stabbed at his eyeballs and he winced. His lips searched for his drinking tube and liquid trickled into his parched mouth as he waited for the pounding in his head to subside.

Without warning everything lurched. His stomach churned and he tasted bile. His head struck the back of his helmet and fresh pain exploded as everything shuddered around him.

How had he arrived here?

Tiny studied the HardSuit opposite. Behind its visor he saw Naina, her eyes closed as though sleeping. Fear jolted, and his stomach lurched as the vehicle was thrown to one side. He knew he had to get out of his HardSuit; he had to find out what was going on. He was no use in the maintenance bay.

As he touched his visor, an image of Tom's lifeless body flashed before his eyes. The memory caused him to catch his breath and he stared at a HardSuit which lay crumpled on the deck before him. Tom's sand-stained helmet lay beside it.

Tiny remembered everything, and a wave of nausea swept over him.

'What the blazes is going on?' Tears welled, the sensation prickling at his eyes. He pushed the emotion back and logic took over: *There has to be a plausible explanation*, he thought. *People don't come back from the dead. It just doesn't happen!*

Tiny stared at the crumpled HardSuit. Red dust lay around it, footprints tracking across the deck plates towards the open hatchway, and for the first time Tiny questioned his own sanity.

This can't be happening; it can't be real. Can it?

CHAPTER 30

Phobos' impact displaced millions of tons of the planet's crust, and the world trembled from pole to pole as a huge rent opened beneath the northern icecap. Magma rushed towards the surface with catastrophic force, and Mars shuddered under the power of its release. Pent-up energies burst forth with such power that the planet wobbled in its orbit, and with a series of judders its polar axis tilted sunwards.

Subjected to ferocious heat, the icecap cracked. Water flooded into deep valleys and raced southwards while clouds of oxygen, water vapour and carbon dioxide shrouded the landscape. The dry atmosphere absorbed the moisture hungrily, and for the first time in billions of years rain clouds formed high overhead.

As Mars finally awakened from its slumber, something buried within its long frozen soil began to stir.

CHAPTER 31

Tiny was thrown into the co-pilot's seat as EV-2's back end slithered around. The vehicle bucked and he was thrown again, a stab of pain causing him to grunt as his ribs struck the edge of the console. He braced himself in his seat and stared at his friend. His head still throbbed as he tried to open a dialogue, but words eluded him.

Ice splattered across the EV's windshield and the light dimmed dramatically. It blinded the vehicle and Tom was forced to reduce speed until it began to clear, the long root-like streaks leaving behind a thick residue of dust and grime.

Tiny leaned forward, his gaze drawn to the swirling patterns beyond the windshield, as ice and slush were forced around submerged boulders and ridges before them. The EV's nose dropped suddenly and a wave spurted upwards as the vehicle settled. The EV jarred against a submerged obstacle, its momentum blocked, and it lurched unexpectedly sideways. Tiny grabbed at his seat harness and buckled himself in, the vehicle carried along by the flow as it twisted sickeningly.

A wall of ice struck the windshield, obliterating their view once more, and Tiny glanced nervously at Tom. His head throbbed with new pain, and after a moment he reached for a medical kit.

The EV's wheels bumped against rocks and debris and the vehicle spun again. It came to a juddering halt and Tom revved the engines until the wheels caught. Another icy surge threw itself against the hull of the vehicle as though attempting to hold it back, and the EV struggled to escape. Its wheels slipped, but finally they dragged the vehicle onto solid ground and it surged forward.

Although not designed to cope with such conditions, the EV was a credit to its designers. *If only they could see it now*, thought

Tiny, *how proud they would be*. EV-2 had been their saviour: without it they would be dead. He only hoped the crew of EV-1 had been as lucky.

At last he opened his mouth to speak, but, before he could, Tom glanced over.

'I'm not dead.'

'What?'

'I said, I'm not dead.'

Tiny felt uncomfortable. His voice trembled. 'But you were.'

Tom tightened his lips before he answered, his manner accompanied by a *so-so* expression. 'Well, sort of.'

Tiny was flustered; Tom's words made no sense. 'What do you mean - how can you be *sort* of dead?' He struggled with the revelation, his words tumbling out in a confused splutter. 'You're either dead or you're not: you can't be both!'

Tom nodded. 'I know what you mean, but believe me, I was only *sort* of dead.' He paused and raised a hand. 'It's a contradiction, I know, but I'll try and explain it later. Now isn't the right time.'

Tiny took a deep breath, opened his mouth to object, then clamped it shut. He rubbed his temples and turned back to the window as he waited for the painkillers to take effect. He folded his arms in defiance.

'And another thing...' he faced his friend again. 'What did you do back there? I mean, how did we end up here?' He indicated the EV. 'The last thing I remember is that wave of ice above us...and then the maintenance bay. *That* doesn't make sense either!'

'Like I said, I'll explain it later: I'm sure Naina will want to know.' Tom paused. 'Anyway, hadn't you better go and check on her? She's probably conscious by now.'

Tiny remained seated for a few seconds before fumbling with his harness. He clambered to his feet. 'Okay,' he said, his voice filled with exasperation, 'but try and keep this damn thing level will you? I'm starting to feel sea sick or Mars sick...or whatever you call it!'

CHAPTER 32

It took over three hours for EV-2 to crest the ravine. The journey was torturous, fraught with a succession of quakes which caused the vehicle to veer from its intended route, but finally they began to leave the rubble-strewn ice behind.

The temperature inside the EV rose uncomfortably, and the bedrock swayed unexpectedly beneath them. The sensation was more unpleasant than that caused by the swirling ice, and both men realised the rock beneath them was floating atop a river of molten lava. They could only hope the bedrock beneath them remained stable enough to support their weight. If it cracked they would have no hope of survival.

Tom eased the EV cautiously forward as the bedrock swayed like a boat on a gentle ocean. Gushing rivers of magma spewed to their left as a fissure gave way under their weight, the EV forcing the precariously balanced plate to sway, and the cockpit lit up with fiery light. Glowing liquid edged across the surface towards them, and Tom gently coaxed the EV away to the right in an effort to place distance between them and the molten rock.

Apart from the sound of the air conditioners, the cockpit was silent. Both men sat bathed in sweat, their flight suits a second skin, but neither spoke. It took a while before the ground began to feel more solid, and Tom was able to increase the EV's speed. 'I think we're coming out of it,' he said. Sweat glistened across his face and he wiped his brow. 'For a few minutes it was touch and go.'

Tiny massaged his eyes and slumped back into the seat. 'Yeah,' he said quietly. He twisted in his seat. 'Thanks.'

A quiet voice from behind took them by surprise, the *thank you* timid, but heartfelt. Naina smiled weakly, but avoided Tom's eyes. The sight of him at the wheel made her feel uncomfortable, and she didn't want to interact with him just yet: it was still too soon.

She turned to the communications board – more to break the tension of the moment than for any practical reason - and busied herself with its switches. She would find her own time to talk things over, but it would have to be when she was ready.

After two hours, Naina dropped her earpiece onto the workstation like a useless relic. 'Well, that's it,' she said. 'There's nothing out there.' She closed her eyes and massaged her temples in an attempt to rub away the remnants of a nagging headache, then climbed wearily into one of the comfier seats. The grim realisation that she would probably die out here, alone and out of contact with everyone she had ever known, was unbearable. She felt herself slip towards desperation and wrapped her arms tightly around her legs. Her own comfort was all she had left.

The icy wind which threw itself against the vehicle added to her sense of gloom, but the persistant motion lulled her, and for a while her thoughts drifted.

The sky turned a deeper colour as the planet turned towards night. The terminator between daylight and darkness which raced towards them was something they anticipated with fear; surviving the events of the day had challenged every ounce of their training and inner strength, but survival at night could easily turn out to be impossible.

As the first hints of dusk approached, a hail of stones clattered across the roof of the EV. The noise was hollow and followed quickly by a *whoosh*, the sound thin in the sparse Martian atmosphere. It startled them. A heavy *whump* followed, with three more in quick succession, and the sound rang through the EV's insulated walls as the vehicle vibrated. Additional impacts struck the landscape and the vehicle jostled.

Naina stumbled to the front of the vehicle, her face ashen with fear. 'What's going on?'

Tiny cupped his hands against the windshield as he struggled to see through the layer of grime. He squinted into the half light, straining to see in the twilight which masked much of the world beyond, until a large shadow filled the sky above. It dropped quickly to the horizon and slammed into the landscape, its impact throwing up thick clouds of debris which fell noisily across the vehicle.

Already strapped in, Tom was spared the worst. Tiny and Naina grabbed for support as the EV pitched violently beneath them. Another rock struck the ground to their right and a hail of fist-sized boulders showered the roof. They scraped across the outer skin of the EV before tumbling to the ground. It was a sound which filled them with dread.

Calm descended, the assault briefly over before a barrage of house-sized rocks obliterated the fading daylight. The force of their impact was devastating, their razor sharp fragments scouring the surface of the planet with a hail of stone shrapnel.

Impacts vibrated through the EV and tossed it like a boat on an ocean. Naina screamed, terror gripping every part of her body as she was thrown against the back of the co-pilot's seat. An overhead rail was the only thing that prevented her from serious injury, and as the vehicle recoiled she dragged herself towards the communications desk. She dropped into its empty seat and grappled urgently for the harness.

As she fumbled with the buckle she called Tiny's name, her voice lost in the booming impacts. She tapped his shoulder and he turned to her with eyes full of terror. 'We have to get out of here!' she yelled. 'We have to find cover!'

'I know, but - ' He looked beyond the vehicle's windows, ' - there's nowhere to go. We're gonna get pulverised!'

'There must be something - somewhere we can hide!' Naina was frantic. She didn't want to die this way; not after having survived everything the planet had thrown at them. She tried to swallow but found her throat painfully dry.

Tom swung the vehicle around and pointed it back into the storm. 'We need to go back,' he said. His voice was calm and measured as he gunned the engines.

'Back? Are you crazy?' Naina stared at him, her eyes wide with disbelief. 'You're taking us back *into* the storm?'

Tom's words brought Tiny to his senses. He stared at his friend, seeing but not knowing him. 'What are you doing?' He leaned forward, his voice breaking under the strain. 'Is this some kind of sick joke?'

Tom glanced up. Grains of red sand still coated his hair; it was as though he and the planet were connected, a part of each other. He felt it now more than ever.

'Pull up the maps,' he said hurriedly. 'We passed something not long ago: a cave, an overhang, something we can use. Hurry!'

Tiny didn't move and Tom urged him again. 'Hurry!' His voice showed the first signs of stress, his calm on the brink of slipping.

Tiny stared briefly at the console before punching in the search commands. A three dimensional map flickered before him; its orange contour lines showed the rise and fall of the landscape, a white track snaking its way across the simulation as it showed the EV's position. Tiny's eyes raced over the map but found nothing which looked as though it would offer sanctuary. 'What am I looking for?'

'It'll be on our port side - a small opening in the cliff edge. It's not much, but it should be large enough to shelter us.' Tom glanced over at the map and pointed to a rock face about a hundred metres away. 'It's somewhere down there.'

Another impact sent rocky fragments skittering across the vehicle's outer hull. A huge shockwave battered them and the EV swerved. Its wheels churned against the sloping ground and struggled to grip before biting in. It raced across a slope, bounced hard as it hit level ground, and headed towards a ravine.

The EV raced below ground level, but the shelter was too shallow and their upper hull remained exposed. Naina looked up as an immense shadow fell over them. It darkened the landscape with its terrifying presence, and she closed her eyes; when death came, she hoped it would be as swift as squashing a bug under the heel of her boot. She knew, without question, that this was the moment it was all going to end.

Tiny increased the magnification and the map enlarged. The ATR - or Automatic Terrain Recorder - used high resolution orbital images of the planet, overlaid with the movements of both vehicles and each crew member. It showed the landscape in fine detail, and with it Tiny located a small opening.

He studied the glowing details closely. 'It's about one hundred and seventy metres southwest, but I can't be more accurate than that. The map is three dimensional, but it's missing up-to-date Guardian data: the storm must be blocking their signals.'

A smattering of sand and stones peppered the windshield like bullets, and with a terrifying sound it cracked. A jagged web snaked across the glass, the horrified faces behind it able to do nothing but stare as the cracks spread in lightening jerks.

The windshield held. Tiny felt his chest begin to ache and he released the breath he had been holding. His heart hammered in his throat. 'How many more close shaves?' he groaned. 'How many more?'

He dragged his eyes to the map, but the constant drumming beyond the EV distracted him. He knew he had to find the place Tom had indicated; the potential for disaster was not something he dared think about, and he hunched forward as he studied the map intensely. 'Okay.' He glanced at Tom. 'Another fifty metres.'

'If we manage to stay in one piece long enough,' added Naina. She stared up at the darkening sky, a mere hint of pink and purple lighting the edge of the shadows, but it was enough to show tumbling silhouettes overhead. She shouted a warning as the sky fell, and her stomach churned at the sight.

'I see them! I see them!' Tom wrenched on the wheel as the hail of rocks slammed into the landscape. Others struck the surface to their right, and the vehicle rolled violently onto its port wheels as the shockwave hit.

It was only Mars' low gravity which prevented the vehicle from rolling over. Its starboard wheels left the surface and Tom wrenched at the steering column. The wheels locked under the vehicle's weight, and it was all he could do to hold the EV steady as it trundled forward.

The wheels dug deep into the dirt and the EV rebelled. Tom fought to keep it from rolling further, but another shockwave battered the vehicle and it shuddered once more. For a moment he felt the vehicle roll beyond its centre of gravity, and thought he was going to lose control, but somehow the vehicle's weight rolled back. He struggled to balance the forces acting upon it, and the EV teetered precariously between Mars' weak gravity and its own weight.

They trundled forward another twenty metres before the EV's weight finally tipped it away from its roll point. It fell slowly back onto six wheels with a great crash which sent clouds of dust billowing into the already choked sky, and the EV recoiled violently on its suspension.

Naina was thrown against her harness and the buckle tore open. She felt herself falling in the low gravity, but the sudden motion was enough to catch her off guard and her head struck a bulkhead support. She was briefly aware of the pain of impact, and a swirling sensation of disorientation, before she blacked out.

CHAPTER 33

The EV sat within a narrow cleft in the cliff wall. Hidden from the airborne barrage they could wait out the worst of the storm, but with communications down and loss of contact with the Guardians and Mission Control, the situation didn't look hopeful. If the conditions had been caused by a meteor storm there was every chance the Guardians were gone, crushed like eggshells in the hail of rock, but Tiny sensed there was something darker and more foreboding. It nagged at the back of his consciousness, and he believed Tom knew the truth.

Tiny attended to Naina's head injury. Finally happy that she was comfortable, he moved towards one of the crew couches. The vehicle rocked as the impacts continued, but he didn't seem to notice. He sat and stared at Tom, the silence between them heavy while Tom sprayed a quick-hardening polymer onto the windshield. It embedded itself into the cracks and strengthened the weakened glass, but was only a temporary solution.

Finally, Tiny broke the silence. 'Okay, it's time for the truth. Come on, give it up – how come you're not dead anymore?'

Tom stepped back from the windscreen and dropped the can of sealant into an open locker. Closing it, he took a deep breath and faced his friend. He felt uncomfortable about explaining, and wasn't sure quite where to begin; there was so much. It all seemed a mess, but he had to start somewhere.

Tom slid into an empty seat and rubbed his fingers through his short hair. A dusty cloud formed around his head, a ghostly halo of Martian dust to complement the moment.

'I don't really know,' said Tom, his voice barely more than a whisper. 'No, that's not strictly true: I *think* I know, but I'm not altogether sure where the dreams end and where reality begins.' He sighed in desperation. 'It's such a long, long story.'

'Well I don't think we're going anywhere just yet, do you?' Tiny's reply was sharp, a distrustful edge to his voice, and he steadied himself as another impact rocked the vehicle. The vibrations were less powerful and the volume of impacts seemed to have lessened during the past thirty minutes. He glanced up at the ceiling, as though he could see through it to the world beyond. *Things are looking a little better,* he thought. *Not good, but better.* Dust scuttled across the outer hull as the distant impacts jolted fragments loose from the overhang above. *I just hope this place holds out.*

The men faced each other, their friendship hanging between them, but Tom was undecided over how much he should reveal. He knew that no matter how he explained it, the situation would sound crazy.

Should I play the whole experience down? he thought, *but what is there to hide?* Even so, Tom felt as though he needed a greater personal understanding before he could fully open himself up, even to Tiny and Naina. They had been such a big part of his life for the past ten years, and they were as close as family. He owed them the truth, at least, but how could he explain things he didn't fully understand himself?

The same questions plagued him now, as they had as a young boy: *Why me? What makes me special?* And there was the ultimate question, the driving question which had driven his life so hard since that fateful childhood day: *What else was there to know?*

They had all suffered shocks in the past week, and, by rights, none of them should be alive now, but he suspected the presence protecting him also had something to do with keeping them all alive; at least he hoped as much.

'Well...' Tom decided to limit this first discussion to his apparent death, and leave it at that. There would be time later for talking about his childhood, if they survived.

Tom measured his words carefully. 'Someone – *something* – was in here with me.' He tapped his head. 'It took control. I knew I was dead, I knew I'd hit my head and stopped breathing, but this...*presence*...was watching over me. Somehow it kept me alive.'

'Did it talk to you? Could you see it?'

Tom felt nervous opening the can of worms that was Mr. Lampard, and sensed his friend's eagerness to delve deeper. It bridged the gap between his fear of the unknown and the friendship they had shared for so long.

'If this...presence...kept you alive it must have bypassed all the functions of the body. It must have breathed for you – kept your brain and organs supplied with oxygen - and stimulated your brain. It didn't want you to die.'

Tom looked away. He wasn't good at lying and didn't want his friend to misunderstand.

'Was it like God? Was it some religious presence?' Tiny seemed lost in the possibility, almost expecting it as a logical explanation.

Tom rubbed his hands together and subconsciously steepled his fingers, the gesture religious in meaning but not intended as such on this occasion. He placed the points of his fingers against the underside of his nose and sat for a moment. The silence hung heavily between them and Tiny knew Tom had something momentous to say. He sensed his friend wasn't overtly religious, but thought perhaps he had had some kind of experience and didn't know how to explain it.

It was a well-documented fact that many Apollo astronauts claimed to have experienced life changing moments during their time on the moon. They believed the vision of Earth as a shining orb of light against the inky blackness of space had opened their minds to greatness, and had created a sense of loneliness in the enormity of space and time. It wasn't uncommon amongst astronauts, but when Tom spoke, Tiny was totally unprepared for the response.

'No.' The single word answer was like a gunshot. It jolted Tiny and made his brain tingle. 'It was nothing religious,' said Tom, his voice shallow and tired. He put his hand to his mouth and shook his head again, his eyes never leaving Tiny's. He scraped at his chin, his fingernails rustling through week-long stubble. *The Hobo Look* his mother had called it.

'I don't know how or where to begin,' he said. He paused briefly, then decided to press on. 'It's not something we – you - have any knowledge of.' Tiny was too stunned to realise the importance of a single word buried in Tom's response, and it passed him by. It would only be later that he would realise exactly what Tom had meant.

Tiny stood up and paced the crew compartment, a non-stop babble of question flowing from him, his mind a whirl. When he finally sat down his questioning was more focused. 'So, what are they like? Are they like us, or are they different?

The silence was punctuated by the resounding thud of falling debris, but somehow it seemed insignificant now. For the days and weeks they may have left, one thing was certain: mankind was not alone in the universe. The great question of life beyond Earth at last had an answer. It was just a shame no one on Earth would ever know the truth.

Tom pondered his reply carefully, as the wrong information now would be difficult to correct later.

'They're just as we've come to expect: bipeds, smaller than us, but vastly more intelligent.' He paused; should he divulge their true identity? After all, Tiny had a right to know, but something, *someone*, seemed to be holding him back, cautioning him to exercise restraint. He had an awareness of being directed, chaperoned, and decided to yield to its will for a short while longer.

He must have frowned because Tiny sat forward, concerned for his friend. 'What?'

Tom opened his mouth but was cut short by the crackle of the radio. It hissed, the barely audible whisper of a disaster beacon interwoven with the background static of Mars.

CHAPTER 34

The dust storms which had raged across the planet's surface had ripped away billions of tons of surface dust. Flung high into the atmosphere, it hung suspended by the static of the solar storm and scoured its way across the surface at tremendous speed.

But it was the violent impact of Phobos which created the most damage. The effects of the impact awakened volcanoes which had lain dormant for millions of years. Deep below its surface, the planet began to move.

Stresses from within buckled and cracked the surface, and immeasurable quantities of ice and water were thrust upwards. Vented onto the surface it gushed forward in great waves, and the planet's geography was changed forever.

As the planet awakened, its dust-filled atmosphere whirled. Iron compounds within the dust resonated, and radio signals weakened by the blankets of thick dust echoed uselessly in all directions.

'Ssh! Listen!' Tiny fine-tuned the radio's filters and reduced the background static. The signal rose and fell as the atmosphere shifted, but the sound of an emergency beacon was unmistakeable.

Tom stood at his friend's shoulder as Tiny crouched over the communications board. He reached forward and adjusted a control, but the signal died once more. Both men returned their attention to the communications board, the tension of the moment strong beneath their feelings of elation.

'If *Foothold's* gone, what do we do? Where do we go?' Tiny stared sightlessly at the console.

'I don't know.' Tom stepped away. 'But if we triangulate their position we might be able to attempt a rendezvous.'

Tiny sunk into the comms chair. 'Yeah, I hope you're right.' He didn't have any desire to verbalise the fact that the beacon could also be the last they would ever hear of their friends; the last they would ever hear of anyone from Earth.

Minutes dragged, as though time were itself being stretched, but finally the signal bleeped once again and Tiny looked up. His smile was belief that the survival of their friends might indeed be possible.

Tom clasped him on the shoulder and sat down in front of the ATR as a 3D globe appeared. It spun quickly as it zoomed in on EV-1's location, and then the signal vanished.

CHAPTER 35

After the signal ended, Tom climbed slowly to his feet and moved into the sleeping compartment. Exhaustion overtook him and he lowered himself onto a bunk. He drew the curtains, enclosed himself in darkness, and within seconds felt himself slide towards sleep.

His rest was disturbed by a jumble of dreams. Faces and memories flooded his mind, their shadows merging one with another, and for the first time in many years he dreamt of Annie.

During his childhood years he had found himself thrust along a new path, and Annie had been there. Her presence had helped him through his adolescence, but he had felt unable to share his experiences with her. He had always kept something back, had always felt it wasn't right to share everything with her, as though it might push her away.

And then his mother had been killed. For eighteen months his life had existed within a devastating, hollow shell. His father had gone to pieces, and although he did his best to be there for Tom and Abi, he had his own grief to deal with. Tom and Abi had quickly found themselves thrust together as siblings, their familiar world thrown into turmoil, but Annie's strength had helped them both.

Annie had become the anchor for Tom's existence, and their lives had become entwined. At times it felt as though they could read each other's thoughts, could anticipate each other's every move, but throughout it all Tom sensed something else – something deeper, something hidden, but despite everything he could never identify precisely what it was.

Annie drifted away, and for a while his sleep was dreamless. When another presence approached he recognised it instantly, and rose to meet it. It was Abi. Her company in his dreams had always strengthened him, and when he awoke his compartment was filled with her memory and the delicate scent of a perfume he knew to be Annie's. Tom smiled through his tears, but his memories were more painful than they had ever been.

Tiny and Naina were deep in discussion when Tom entered, coffee mugs and discarded food wrappings evidence of a prolonged discussion. Tom knew he had slept longer than he had intended.

Naina glanced up as Tom poked his head into the compartment and regarded him with a knowing look. Her gaze told him Tiny had filled her in on the details while he slept; that made matters a little easier, but he wasn't ready to face Naina just yet.

With a half smile, Tom moved to the galley. He prepared a quick breakfast and moved towards the cockpit to eat in privacy.

Tiny shuffled in and sat down, the atmosphere awkward, but as Tom ate they ran through the preliminary plans Tiny and Naina had made towards the rendezvous with EV-1. Their journey certainly wouldn't be as smooth as it had been on the way out, and many of the details were nothing more than vague outlines. The combination of surface activity, high winds and aerial bombardment would no doubt have made dramatic changes to the topography of the landscape. They would just have to deal with things as their journey unfolded.

After Tiny left, Tom sat alone with only his thoughts for company. The EV rocked gently as faint impacts vibrated through the vehicle's hull, but were so faint he hardly felt them.

He pulled a DataPad from his pocket and began absently flicking through his personal image files. He opened a folder of photographs and smiled: Abi and he at the launch site, the huge rocket stack behind them only weeks before the launch date; his father wearing Tom's mission cap, the *Foothold* emblem emblazoned across it as he tucked into a hearty steak dinner; and his Mum. His smile faded.

His mother's eyes seemed to smile back at him from that day

almost thirty years ago, her face an eternal picture of youth and beauty as she sat on the stone wall behind the Old Vicarage. He remembered the moment he had taken the photo, and the conversation they had shared. It cut like a blade across the years.

Deep in concentration, Tom was startled as a gentle hand warmed the back of his neck. He looked up to see Naina slide into the seat alongside him, her smile comforting. She nodded her head as she spoke. 'It's okay,' she said. 'Tiny has explained everything to me. I can't say I understand – neither of us does – but we're your friends regardless. I'm just sorry I freaked earlier.' She paused and took Tom by the hand, her face apologetic. 'It was bad enough when I knew you were dead, but then you were...' She squeezed his hand and leant over to kiss him gently on the cheek. 'Well, you know,' she said. And with that, she was gone.

CHAPTER 36

It took three days before the bombardment calmed sufficiently for the EV to venture from its shelter. When it did, the world awaiting them was vastly different from the one they had left behind.

A misty veil hung over the whole landscape; a shroud of vapour which stirred as the winds whipped in blustery squalls. Parting before them as the vehicle nudged forward, the mists gave way to a rocky landscape which was oddly tilted. New highlands stretched up into the mist to their right and rolling plains fell away to their left. Much of the surface sand had been whipped away by the storms to leave exposed bedrock, a rippled testimony to the planet's history of volcanic activity.

The EV turned towards the highlands and increased speed. It pulled away, slipping here and there between the corrugations in the rock, but settled into a steady rhythm as its wheels left the ridges behind and moved onto smooth surfaces. Tom gave Naina a big smile as they rose higher, the stressful opening minutes of their ride soon behind them, and they settled into a steady pace.

After several hours they reached level ground at the top of the hill range, and the mist increased. Tiny slowed the EV to a crawl and they navigated their way around a fresh crater, the ridges which spread outwards from it evidence of powerful impacts.

A vent gaped in the crater's southernmost edge. Torn apart by forces from within it lay open to the sky, and Naina climbed quickly into the observation blister atop the vehicle. From her high vantage point she had a clear view inside, and as she watched, the rocky interior of the planet welled upwards like the tongue of a sleeping giant. Rubble tumbled over itself as it was forced through the throat of the vent in streams of dust-encrusted ice-water. It oozed as though a living substance desperate to leave the world beneath. Liquid water, warmed by some different route, gushed from another opening and tumbled away in a spectacular waterfall.

'This is incredible.' Naina stood on tip toes, attempting to increase her height by vital centimetres as she peered deep into the crater.

'It's only the start. Look.' Tom stood against the starboard viewing port, entranced as the mists parted to allow him a brief views across the rolling plains below.

He was transfixed as the world appeared briefly once more, but had seen enough to understand the planet was now a tantalisingly different world to the one they had travelled so far to explore.

* * *

Under normal conditions their journey should have taken about three days, but the new surface conditions dictated that every moment be driven with extreme caution. The EV's Auto Pilot was useless and Tiny's carefully laid plans were soon abandoned. Every twist and turn of the landscape presented a new challenge, and a test of nerve which needed the human touch.

The Martian surface had buckled under pressures from within and had opened in many places across the landscape. On several occasions the EV had to drive kilometres out of its way in order to navigate whole fields of blast holes, but every kilometre travelled was a scientist's dream.

Cresting a ridge they found the surface increasingly sandy and rubble-strewn, with ejecta from impact craters and volcanic eruptions heaped across the landscape. New hill ranges had formed as a result of the intense sub-surface pressures, and upwelling lava had moulded peaks and troughs which dropped away into deep valleys. It was a world of fresh and exciting promise.

The emergence of ice and liquid water from beneath the surface had transformed the dried up river beds and plains. It had run across the hillsides in torrents, filled valleys and dust bowls, and created an entirely new landscape.

But the sudden up-thrust had exposed more than just water and ice to the thickening Martian atmosphere. Dormant seeds, buried since life had been ripped from the red planet long ago, now soaked up ultraviolet rays from the distant sun as they lay across the water-soaked landscape. Purple hair-like shoots anchored each seed to hairline cracks which criss-crossed the ground, and acorn-like buds sprouted from their fast-growing stems. The buds would soon open like Earthly flowers, basking in the weak sunlight, before casting millions of tiny seeds across the barren landscape in a display of explosive reproduction.

It was the first life to grow on Mars since the planet had died three billion years ago. This time it would survive.

* * *

By the middle of their fourth afternoon they had descended onto a flat plain. Even at high altitude the rocky landscape showed clear evidence of the scouring erosion of water and ice, but most had drained into the lowlands. What did remain had pooled into thin sheets of surface water, but very little ice remained; it was clear evidence of accelerated warming across the surface of the planet.

Tiny had disappeared for a nap several hours ago, leaving

Tom to drive while Naina dozed in the co-pilot's seat. Tiny had driven more than his fair share, and had been so exhausted when Tom had taken over that he had headed straight for his bunk.

Driving allowed Tom to be alone with his thoughts; he had much to think about and needed to deal with the staggering developments at his own pace.

'I've made a decision,' he said finally. His words roused Naina from a doze and she frowned as she pulled herself back to consciousness. 'A decision - about what?'

'About what's happened. You know Riordan is by-the-book. He'll want to keep me out of the loop, keep me in the background, and I don't know quite how he'll react to the full story.'

Naina considered Tom's logic. Jack Riordan was a bit of a stickler for rules and regulations, even this far from home, but was a good man nevertheless. He was undoubtedly the best Commander the mission could have had, but wasn't known as the most pliable member of the crew. He would probably deal with the truth as though Tom were some kind of enemy. It wouldn't be good.

'That's probably a good idea - at least for now - but you can't keep him in the dark forever.'

'Glad you agree.' Tom smiled and relaxed a little.

A long pause hovered between them and Tom sensed Naina had another question.

'So, what *are* you going to tell them?' She folded her arms and rested her knees on the edge of the console.

Tom paused. 'Nothing.'

'Nothing?'

'We can't turn back the clock, so why give them something else to worry about? If we don't tell, then we can concentrate on the issues that really matter. We have enough problems to deal with without adding any more into the mix.' Tom adjusted their course slightly and then continued. 'Let's face it, our prospects aren't exactly glowing at the moment: *Foothold* is undoubtedly gone, we have limited food stocks and no means of transportation off this rock. Sure, we can generate enough water, oxygen and heat to keep us going indefinitely, but it's no good without food. Unless Earth realises we are still alive and sends an express galactic food parcel, we're done for. So, like I said, why tell them anything?'

Naina nodded. 'Do you think Tiny will go along with it? If he doesn't...'

'Ah, you leave him to me. He owes me a favour or two, even if *he's* forgotten about them.' Tom winked and gave a knowing smile. 'But I haven't.'

Naina laughed, her mood lighter. 'So, we just deal with the here and now, the *'Hi,-how-are-you-getting-along-now-we're-on-our-own-on-an-alien-planet-millions-of-kilometres-from-home* approach?"

Tom twisted his mouth as he summed everything up, and then smiled. 'Yeah. Something like that.'

'Anyway, what's to say *they* haven't had a similar experience? They could be thinking the same as us right now.'

Tom sniggered. 'That I *don't* think.'

'How do you know?' Naina twisted in her seat, her back still sore from the burns she'd received a few days previously. She studied Tom with a more serious air and had the distinct impression that he knew more than he was letting on.

* * *

Tom came instantly awake as the vehicle rolled to a standstill. The mist had closed in once again and it looked as though they were immersed in low cloud.

'Why have we stopped?' He levered himself up from the seat where he had been sleeping. 'What's going on?'

'I'm not sure, but we can't drive any further until this mist clears. It's too dangerous.' Naina was grateful for the break and felt her shoulders click as she stretched. The pilot's chair wasn't the most comfortable seat in the EV. She'd complained about it during the design stage, but the engineers had decided to fit a standard seat rather than a heavily cushioned design. Even on a mission as sophisticated as *Foothold*, they'd had to save money somewhere.

Tom cupped his hands to his face as he peered out of the window. 'What did you see? What was it?'

'I don't know. It looked for a second as though there were something out there; some kind of structure.' Naina gestured with her hands, drawing a spiral-like column in the air. 'It was tall, but I didn't get a clear view.'

Tiny's voice startled them both. They hadn't heard him enter the cockpit. 'Was it natural?'

Naina didn't turn her eyes from the windscreen. 'I don't know.'

'Well,' said Tiny, his face a mask of schoolboy excitement. 'I don't know about you two, but *I'm* gonna take a look! You coming?'

CHAPTER 37

Three suited figures stepped into the fog and all but vanished. Visibility was extremely low and there was every chance the ground had been broken up by the volcanic activity, so Tiny strung a tether between them for safety. If anyone fell it could be fatal.

The mist parted around them as they moved forward. Naina waved her hand and watched as the thick vapour moved slowly between her gloved fingers. It was a heavy vapour and she set her computer to work analysing it.

Tom rubbed his feet through the surface dust and found it thicker, more damp and clumpy than before, like wet beach sand. It clung to his boots in a coarse layer and he bent down to scoop some into a sample container.

Tiny took electromagnetic and radiation readings. 'We haven't got long out here, guys. Radiation is still on the high side, so let's not waste any time.' He led off into the mist and both Tom and Naina felt their tethers pull taut as he moved away, but could do nothing other than follow.

The ground was heavily creased beneath their feet, as though it had been forced apart to allow something to pass through. Tom had a sense he had seen it before, but couldn't grasp where. It was like a dream, just out of reach after waking.

A skittering sound caused Tom to look up and he saw a cloud of dust as it fell slowly across his faceplate. It reminded him of a snow flurry. Naina's voice filled his ears. 'What goes up must come down.' She smiled, the falling dust casting a thin veil between them.

'Well I hope it comes down gently,' said Tom. 'There's a lot to fall.'

'Yeah. If it comes down suddenly we could end up buried.'

Tiny faced them, his suited form only just visible in the falling dust and the mist.

Tom gazed back into the sky and drank in the sight as something struck his faceplate. A heavy *splat!* caused him to jump back. He expected a fall of pebbles or dust from the suspended clouds, but as another impact stuck his helmet he yelled in excitement. Something he had never expected to see on Mars snaked across his visor.

Tiny's voice was loud in Tom's ears, the voice cut short as the ground erupted with a series of small impacts. Tiny turned his face to the sky, the mist before him suddenly streaked with angular lines whose paths terminated in fat circular marks. They soaked immediately into the parched ground, and as Tom watched his vision was distorted by rivulets of liquid which ran across his visor. Surface tension dragged the droplets together into ragged lines, and played them across his vision like streaks of blood.

Laughter filled his earpiece, and Tom looked around to find Naina with her gloved palms upwards, her face alive with wonder. Tiny turned a slow circle before him, his arms held wide as though embracing the moment. The comms channel was filled with whoops of laughter and excited chatter.

Tom looked up through his dust-streaked visor, and smiled.

It was raining.

* * *

The rain fell like a red mist. It ran in slow rivulets across the shells of their HardSuits, crafting intricate patterns in the dusty stains which lingered from months of exposure to Mars' harsh environment.

For minutes a barrage of questions flowed between them, but eventually they fell silent as the mist began to thin. The sight that greeted them stunned all three astronauts into silence.

Silhouetted against the haze, their true height hidden by the misty atmosphere, stood a forest of columns. Their truncated bases stood solid, tree-like with a girth thicker than a man's waist, but their irregular forms angled upwards like the columns of some vast gothic cathedral. Their immense height seemed to twist and distort the landscape from which they grew, and the figures beneath suddenly felt very small.

Charged with static electricity during the storms, particles of airborne dust had clumped together, forming towering columns high into the sky. As the storms had increased in ferocity they had deposited clumps of charged dust across the planet's surface, and the columns had grown.

'Are they solid?' Tiny reached out, his gloved fingers hovering above a column. 'Shall I?' He glanced at Tom and Naina, unsure what to do.

'Might as well.' Tom shrugged and Tiny laid his fingertips on the surface. Held together by static, the touch of his earthed body was all the column needed, and it fell to the ground in a cloud of spluttering dust.

'Woa! Didn't expect that. What happened?' Tiny stood with his hand frozen before him like a child who has just knocked over a priceless vase in an antique shop.

Tom flipped on his suit computer, data scrolling across the inside of his visor as he took readings of another column. He'd barely started when Naina spoke. 'Static,' she said. 'Nothing but static.'

'Static? Well, that's something to write home about...' He realised what he'd just said and cringed. 'Sorry.' He dropped his voice but Naina continued as though she hadn't heard.

'It's the atmosphere. The storm must have created a flood of highly charged particles. They're dissipating now, but static charge is what's holding these structures together.' She looked at Tiny. 'We just happened to come along and ground the charge.'

'Like a lightening conductor.'

'Mm-hmm. That's us: an intergalactic lightening rod.' Naina looked around. 'The other columns will collapse as their charge weakens. If you hadn't touched it, the structure would have eventually fallen itself. We just happened to give it a nudge.'

'Well that makes me feel better. I'd hate to think I'd come all this way just to destroy some totally unique phenomenon by being careless. Try explaining that one away!'

Tom unclipped his harness as Naina studied another column, and walked with Tiny towards the edge of the clearing. Together they gazed into the swirling mist, and for an instant it cleared. Before them a valley stretched out like a giant furrow.

'What was that?' Tiny's attention had been drawn to something half seen.

'What was what? Where are you looking?'

Tiny pointed. 'Down there. Didn't you see it? Something shining on the slope below us.'

Tom shook his head. 'Didn't see anything.' He willed the mists to clear once more, but they remained closed in. 'What did it look like?'

Tiny took his time before replying. He couldn't quite explain - it had looked like a flat surface, but that could just be the refection of sunlight off the surface of an angular crack in a rock, its crystalline insides gleaming in the light of its first Martian day. *No. That's not right*, he thought. *It was something else. Something...constructed.*

It couldn't be something artificial, could it? But after what had happened to Tom, there was every possibility. He studied Tom's face and decided to play it safe. He didn't want to look a fool if it really were something natural. 'It looked...I don't know, out of place; something that shouldn't be there.'

The mists thinned a little and a crumbling and battered vista revealed itself. Rounded peaks nosed their way out of the mist as though breathing the atmosphere.

'There! You see that?' Tiny almost spat the words, his relief evident as something flickered in the mist. It quickly vanished then appeared once more, its light bright yet too intense to be a reflection of the weak sun overhead. Flickering through the misty cover the object remained tantalisingly hidden, but a strengthening wind gusted through the valley and the mist dissipated. It was as though a great hand had swept aside a curtain of mystery and laid the landscape bare before them.

Tiny's voice cut through the silence, his voice hesitant. 'Now what...is *that?*'

Tom studied the light. It flickered and dimmed. 'I have no idea. But it's moving.'

'What's moving?' The conversation had caught Naina's attention and she stepped up beside them.

'We're not sure.' Tiny turned towards her. 'But whatever it is, it's moving at a decent speed.'

A light breeze pushed away the last remnants of mist and the valley opened before them again. It glowed salmon pink and brown, its ochre shadows deepening to purple against the empty landscape as it rolled towards the distant horizon. It was a desolate landscape littered with fresh impact craters and rubble from the recent bombardment. Something glinted in the early morning sun; a flash of light that repositioned itself as it moved.

The reflection vanished behind a large boulder, the uneven ground hindering its progress, and the light flickered several times before appearing again as brightly as before. Large boulders obscured the light's appearance, and Tiny made a sound of irritation as he lost sight of it once more.

He shuffled position and flipped his binocular visor into place, the scene enlarging into extreme close-up as he adjusted the magnification.

The shape remained shielded by the boulder field, but at last broke free and changed course towards the top of the hill. Its reflections hid the object's true shape, as though shrouded inside a cocoon of light, and Tiny studied the object carefully before he spoke again. His voice was slow, his words measured. 'Well, it's not an EV - it's way too big. And it looks to be the wrong shape, but I can't see it clearly enough.' He paused, irritated. 'That light's too damned bright!'

Tom clicked his own binocular visor into place and studied the object. It moved as though deliberately distorting itself, then a layer of mist covered it and the scene faded completely.

When it reappeared, Tom stepped back suddenly and stowed his binocular visor. His heart hammered in his chest. A faint presence - not unlike an unexpected flavour, half tasted but familiar – suddenly appeared on his tongue, and it startled him.

'What is it? What's the matter?' Tiny's voice was husky, his own nerves betraying him.

Tom sipped from his drinking tube and attempted to blank out the taste. Its origin was familiar, like the smell of an old house visited for the first time in years; an aftertaste which caught at the back of his throat. The presence faded, but he was left with an all-consuming sense that something was wrong.

'I don't know,' he said. He looked up nervously. 'But I think we're about to find out.'

CHAPTER 38

It crested the hill silently, crawling its way across the last few metres until it reached level ground. It dwarfed the three standing figures with its huge bulk, blocking out the sky and casting a deep shadow across the hilltop as it slowed to a standstill.

The hull design was not dissimilar to that of a stingray, its upper surface flat like the wings of the ocean-bound creature, but its underside arched downwards into a great bulge. Its reflective surface threw back a distorted image of the landscape, broken only by the huge treads which held the whole structure off the ground. Each tread stood more than two metres wide and taller than a man, and was attached to the main body by a heavy suspension system which supported the whole assembly.

A series of needle-like probes and sensors poked their way from the leading edge of the upper hull, while a bank of cutting and drilling tools adorned the space between the treads. Their cutting surfaces were serrated and twisted, like the ferocious mandibles of some unknown beast.

To the casual observer the vehicle had the look of a machine of exploration, one constructed for a harsh environment like the deepest oceans of Earth, yet it was a design unlike anything the three astronauts had ever seen before.

The vehicle remained motionless for long minutes, its presence intimidating and oppressive. Tom, Naina and Tiny huddled together in its shadow, their conversation hurried and nervous. Finally, his heart drumming heavily in his chest, his blood pumping and his breathing short and ragged, Tom stepped forward. He raised his hands, palms uppermost, and waited.

The enormity of the situation hung heavily around him. *What are the implications of first contact with visitors from another world?*

He recalled his past encounters with the An'Tsari, with their great black ship and blinding lights, but this was different. Back then, only a few people had witnessed their arrival. They had invaded his childhood, their presence unwanted and aggressive as they reached out to take back what had been theirs, and they had removed knowledge of their existence from everyone but him.

It had been terrifying.

The knowledge of their existence had weighed heavily upon his life; it had been like baggage he could not discard, a weight he had been forced to carry, and now the prospect terrified him all over again.

Over the past ten days everything he knew had been ripped apart. The being which had shown him so much, the figure which had been with him throughout, was now strangely absent, unless he was on the vehicle before him. But if that were true, why had Mr. Lampard led Tom to believe that he was the only member of the An'Tsari still alive?

Is this it? Tom thought. *Is this what you sent me here to find, or have you been hiding the truth all along?* Tom looked up at the vehicle, its silver flanks glimmering in the morning light. *Are you waiting for me inside?*

Tom listened to his inner thoughts. *Where are you? What do you want from me? I've come all this way and now you refuse to show yourself. Why?*

A realisation cut through Tom's inner questions like a knife. *What if the truth isn't ready to be revealed just yet?* He felt the sudden weight of the knowledge he possessed and understood the responsibility that came with it. He turned back to his friends, their faces visibly strained.

A voice crackled in his earpiece. 'What's wrong?'

Tom shook his head, the gesture hidden by the bulk of his helmet. 'Nothing. I was just wondering...' His voice trailed off and he shook his head again. 'It's nothing. Forget it.'

Before the events of the past few weeks, only Tom had known the truth about the existence of alien life. Now, the truth stood before them all. If he had spoken out about what had happened during his childhood he would have been farmed off as some kind of crackpot, some kind of alien conspiracy theory nut, and would never have made it past the gates of NASA. He most certainly wouldn't have made it into the astronaut training program. Now, after everything that had happened, the fact that Mr. Lampard had presented knowledge of the An'Tsari's existence only to Tom indicated the momentous importance of such a secret. Keeping that knowledge hidden until the time was right to inform the human race of its origins suddenly made perfect sense.

What was it he'd been told all those years ago? *You will understand.* The voice sounded as clear in his head now as it had when he'd been ten years old. Somehow he'd never forgotten it. His mind had echoed it over and over, reliving it like the opening of a long forgotten box of memories, like the scent of old toys and faded books.

But what do I say to these beings? he thought. *What do I say when I meet them face to face, not in my head or my dreams, but when I actually stand on the rocky surface and see them with my own eyes? What can any man say?*

Tom dropped his hands slowly as he pondered his choices. *Welcome*, he thought. *We represent the combined peoples of planet Earth.* He considered the words carefully. *Are they too formal; too political?*

Tom stepped forward and cleared his throat. He raised his palms upwards once more in a gesture of peace, and worked to keep his voice strong and level. It was imperative his words were clear, their meaning sincere. This was undoubtedly the greatest moment in the history of the human race, and he couldn't afford it to be marred by a simple misunderstanding.

From somewhere he found an inner calm, and his words came out with confidence and strength. 'We are explorers from planet Earth,' he began. 'On behalf of all the combined peoples of our home planet, may I offer you the hand of friendship and peace?'

His gloved hands remained upturned.

'Welcome.'

CHAPTER 39

Tom waited. Blood pumped hard inside his head and he felt every intake of breath as though it were his last. Did they not understand him? Were they ignoring him?

What do I do now? He turned to his friends. Naina shook her head and raised her arms in bewilderment.

'Check your frequencies. Try again.' Tom checked his radio; it was already set to wide-band. Unless they had chosen not to respond, his message must have been received.

'Okay.' He turned back to the vehicle and spoke again. His voice was confident.

'We are explorers from planet Earth. On behalf of all the combined peoples of our home planet, may I...'

Movement caught his eye and his words tailed off. A figure, its body silhouetted black against the light, moved towards him under the belly of the towering vehicle. It shuffled across the dusty ground and halted about five metres away.

The figure wore a black and grey pressure suit which was more streamlined than his own, its appearance more advanced. Across the chest was an instrument panel from which a number of familiar-looking umbilical hoses sprouted, but there were also connections Tom did not recognise. The figure was stocky and stood about the normal height of a man, yet something immediately seemed out of place. For a second Tom sensed a familiar presence, a watchfulness, but then it was gone. The figure took a step forward and Tom saw himself reflected in the darkness of the faceplate.

Sunlight reflected off exposed metal and an emblem caught Tom's attention. He frowned and leaned forward to read the patch; it showed two circles interlocked upon a dark background, their pattern similar to a figure eight with the digits of the number twelve separated by a red disc. Across the chest panel a name was emblazoned in white lettering: Forrestal.

A voice filled Tom's earpiece, but he did not register the words immediately. Tiny and Naina approached slowly as the words were repeated, the voice clear with little hint of an accent. 'Are you okay?'

'Yes, I...' Tom was suddenly at a loss for words. The figure unclipped its tinted visor and slid it upwards. The face behind had dark hair, with a thick layer of stubble covering its square features. Forrestal stepped forward.

Tiny's question filled the silence. 'Who are you?' Forrestal didn't respond and Tiny moved towards the suited figure. 'You're obviously human, and somehow I don't think you're from anywhere other than Earth.' He paused, but Forrestal didn't respond. 'How long have you been here?' he asked. 'Which organisation are you from? Who sent you?'

'Too many questions, but you will be told what you need to know.'

Tiny dipped his head towards Forrestal, his face clouded by barely concealed distrust. 'What we *need* to know?' He took another step. 'What we need to know?' He snorted, disbelief evident in every word. He glanced towards Tom and Naina as he spoke. 'Now, you listen to me. We've spent seven months travelling tens of millions of kilometres, have been separated from our family and friends, faced hardship and danger, only to find there's someone else here! And then, to top it all off, that person tells me we will be told what we *need* to know!' He flung his arms wide. 'Do you have any idea how angry, how *betrayed*, we feel right now?'

Tiny paused but the figure did not respond. 'Someone up there has led us a right merry dance.' He gestured above his head as he spoke. 'Someone has taken us all by the hand and led us down the garden path!'

He paused again and took several deep breaths in an effort to calm himself. When he continued his voice was more controlled. 'Do you have any idea how many years we've spent preparing for this mission? How many years we've built ourselves up and struggled to be at the top of our game, just so we can stand here? And now, to top it all off, the whole planet has gone whacko and our only means of permanent survival are a crushed spacecraft and an ailing EV. Our friends are either dead or dying somewhere on this godforsaken planet, and you have the nerve to stand there and talk down to me!' Tiny was angrier than Tom had ever seen him, and Tiny pushed the figure as he spoke. 'Now I'm telling *you*, we want some answers, and we want them *now!* How long have you been here and which organisation are you from?'

Forrestal was unfazed. 'And I told you, you will be told what you need to know.' His voice was calm and steely. 'Take it from me, you don't know whom you are dealing with, and you don't want to cross us. Fact.'

'We don't know whom we're dealing with? Now that sounds like a threat,' Tiny's voice took on a distinctive growl, 'and I don't like being threatened. Right, I'm going to ask you one more time: who are you?'

Tom appeared at Tiny's side. His voice was calm and matter of fact. 'Black Project. It has to be.' Tiny's glare didn't leave Forrestal's eyes as Tom spoke. 'A top secret research project, funded by a black budget and run by people with power above that of the world's leaders. These projects exist, but their existence is denied.' Tom stepped forward and met Forrestal's gaze. 'Fact.'

Tiny continued. 'So which country is funding you? Which country is your base of operations?' Tom's explanation had struck the mark. '*Whom* do you represent?' Sarcasm filled Tiny's voice.

'Like I said,' the figure stood his ground, 'you will be told what you need to know. Now...' he indicated the back of the vehicle.

Tom switched off his radio and drew his crewmates away from Forrestal. He pulled them in and they all touched helmets so their voices could vibrate between them. 'Whether you believe him or not, we're all here together and our first priority is survival,' he said.

Naina agreed. 'They're obviously better equipped than we are, so it makes sense to pull together. At least until we know more.'

The vehicle was radically different from their own. As they left the airlock Tom, Naina and Tiny passed through a series of corridors and bulkheads, but saw no other crew members. Forrestal did not speak, and neither did the crew of the EV, but Tiny stayed close on Forrestal's heels. He was impatient for answers and mad as hell, but Forrestal seemed not to notice.

After walking for nearly five minutes they arrived at a spacious Command Centre. Its twelve workstations were arranged in a wide shell and illuminated by the glow from multiple VDU screens, yet all were vacant. Walkways between the stations were picked out with floor mounted lights, diamond bright in the darkness, and in the centre of the room, on a raised dais, stood the Commander's station.

A 3D image of Mars dominated the upper left quadrant of the Commander's screens. Other images and streams of data overlapped, while on a screen to the far right sat an image of EV-2.

'Wait here.' Forrestal's stepped up onto the dais and bent to speak to a figure hidden within the shadows. The figure turned slowly, silhouetted against the light of the screens, and inspected the visitors as one might study some lower form of life. Finally, the figure climbed slowly to its feet and stepped down onto the main deck.

The figure was tall with an air of superiority, an air of impatience with those before him, and Tom knew instantly that they were not going to get on.

CHAPTER 41

'Harriman.' The big man did not smile.

'Captain? Major?' Tiny looked for some indication of rank on the jumpsuit, but found none.

'Just Harriman. This isn't a military operation.' Harriman shook hands briefly with Naina and Tiny before taking hold of Tom's. The hand he offered was cool, the handshake weak and unconvincing. Tom didn't like the sensation; its dry skin gave him a brief jolt, like a static shock. It felt wrong.

'So, if you're not a military operation, who's funding you?' Tom stared directly at Harriman as he asked the question and saw the other man's jaw tighten. Tom's initial impression was that Harriman would give them no more information than Forrestal already had.

'That information is classified. All that matters is that we exist.'

Tiny bristled, barely concealed anger bubbling under the surface. His words were sharp. 'Despite what you think, the fact that you exist is our concern. We came here as representatives of Earth on a mission of peace and exploration, yet here you are, acting as though the planet is yours already, as though our presence is an interference.' He folded his arms and pulled himself up to his full height. 'You just expect us to accept what you have told us, but it's simply not enough.'

Harriman studied the crew before him. He looked from face to face. He nodded slightly, his mouth twisted in thought. When he spoke again it was in a different tone: less dismissive and more understanding. 'Okay,' he said. 'We'll talk more, but later. Right now you need food and rest.' He looked at Tom. 'You also need a shower. You stink.'

* * *

They were led through darkened corridors, the deck plates absorbing the sound of their feet as they tramped along in single file. Computer terminals blinked brightly from alcoves along their route, complex graphics decorating their screens, but they showed nothing that made any sense. Each door they passed held an identification plate, but the light level was too dim to allow the panels to be read without closer observation. Nevertheless, Tiny slowed several times and leant in for a closer look: *Minerals Lab*, read one. *Archaeology*, read another. *Archaeology?* Tiny felt a nudge in his back as he slowed, and he turned. 'Steady on,' he said. 'Only looking.'

'Keep moving.' The figure didn't engage in conversation. It was obvious his orders did not include allowing the crew to linger.

Naina beckoned over her shoulder to Tiny and he leant forward. 'Interesting rooms,' she whispered. Tiny raised his eyebrows and nodded, his eyes immediately full of the mischief Naina had seen many times before. When he suddenly stopped walking and turned to the figure behind him, Naina wasn't surprised.

'Hey, this is some operation, man. You want to enlighten us as to what you're doing out here?'

The figure ignored the question. 'Keep moving.'

Tiny held the man's gaze for a moment. 'Okay,' he said chirpily, and then set off again. His long legs soon closed the distance behind Naina, and as they rounded a corner he pulled her back and swapped places. The jump-suited figure rounded the corner and they collided.

'What's in here? What are you hiding?' Naina leaned in for a closer look at a doorplate, shielding their guide's view of the corridor. *'Cryptography?* What can you possibly have found on Mars that needs decrypting...or encrypting?'

'Move along.' The jump-suit spoke firmly, but Naina stood her ground. 'I said move along. Now.' A firm hand pushed her and she stumbled.

'Hey! You leave the lady alone.' Tiny appeared suddenly from behind, his bulk filling the space between them, and he squared up to the smaller man. Tiny was a full head and a half taller and peered down at the name on the jumpsuit. 'Williams, is it? Well listen, Williams, you leave her alone, you got that? You gotta have respect for the ladies.' He placed his arm in front of Naina and nudged her gently behind him. 'Or you'll have me to deal with. Understand?'

Williams appeared not to hear. 'I said move along.'

Tiny folded his arms and stood his ground, his presence defying the other man to try and come through him. Tiny had the advantage of size, but it was Tom who broke the deadlock. 'Come on, guys,' he said. 'NASA didn't send us all this way just so you could pick a fight. That's not what we're here for.' He clapped Tiny on the back. 'Let it go. Harriman has already said he's going to talk to us.'

Tiny stared down at Williams for a while longer, and then put a big hand on his shoulder. He leant in until they were almost nose to nose. 'Don't mistreat the lady,' he said quietly, his voice no more than a whisper, 'Don't mistreat the lady, 'cuz she'll have you for breakfast.'

Tiny cuffed Williams playfully around the ear, winked, and then turned on his heel and strode away.

They were shown to a communal shower block and given fresh clothing; their white jumpsuits distinguished them as visitors and were much like those they had worn back in astronaut training.

The two men waited respectfully inside a cubicle while Naina showered. Their guards prevented them from leaving by positioning themselves outside the shower block door. 'What do you make of all this?' Tom whispered. He wasn't sure how much they could be overheard.

'This thing is amazing - it's the size of a small base and has the resources to accommodate ten, maybe twelve people.' He pushed his hands into his pockets. It's far beyond anything

NASA has dreamt of. It's almost...' He shook his head and sighed. 'What do you make of it?'

Tom didn't want to think too deeply. Everything about the interior of the vehicle was well designed; surfaces joined seamlessly as though the vehicle had been grown rather than constructed, with walls and floors exhibiting a unique sound absorbing quality. Even the lighting was hidden, the walls and ceiling seemingly lit from within, with a perfect glow in all directions.

Tom shook his head and stared down at his boots. He'd had enough surprises and could do without any more, but there was definitely something about the vehicle; something he sensed within its corridors that resonated within him. 'I don't know,' he said, 'but...' He didn't finish the sentence.

'Yeah,' said Tiny, 'that's just what I thought.'

It felt as though the vehicle had been designed somewhere else.

CHAPTER 42

Harriman led them to a small meeting room after they had showered and eaten, but the atmosphere remained tense.

'First of all,' he said, 'I will not tolerate aggression towards any member of my crew.' He looked directly at Tiny. 'You are here at my discretion and I can just as easily have you returned to your own vehicle to fend for yourselves. Have you got that?'

Tiny nodded. They had no choice but to comply - that much was certain. He sipped his coffee.

Tom diverted the conversation. 'Did you pick up the signal from our other vehicle? Their beacon was brief, but we managed to get a fix on it.'

'That is being attended to. We will keep you informed,' said Harriman.

'Thank you.' Naina was visibly relieved. She smiled. Tom and Tiny shared her relief, the room filled with their excited chatter and emotion as the dark shadow of uncertainty lifted slightly. It was news they needed to hear.

Harriman continued drinking his coffee and waited until the feelings of relief had run their course. Finally, his cup cradled between his hands, he coughed to break the moment and spoke. 'The current situation is this: as I'm sure you're aware, a massive solar flare has struck this planet. It was far greater than anyone could have expected, and was totally unpredicted. As a consequence, dust storms currently cover over two thirds of the surface and the atmosphere has suffered global warming, with temperatures rising between ten and twenty degrees. Heat spots have formed around the equator and ice trapped within the surface dust has begun thawing.'

Naina cut Harriman off. 'But water can't possibly exist on Mars in all three states, the low atmospheric pressure simply won't allow it.' She paused, waiting for Harriman to comment.

When he didn't, she carried on. 'Something else has happened here.'

Harriman glared. He was obviously not used to being cut off. 'If you'll let me finish...'

Naina waved her hands in apology. 'Sorry. Please continue.'

Harriman looked between the faces. His expression showed irritation at being interrupted, but after a lengthy pause he spoke again. 'Eight days ago a major impact destabilised the planet and changed its orbital rotation.'

Three voices spoke as one, their disbelief and anxiety clear amongst the barrage of questions. Tom silenced them with a gesture. 'What precisely does 'changed its orbital rotation' mean?'

For the first time Harriman seemed uncomfortable. Tom saw his appearance distort and squirm as though he was uneasy, his physical appearance transformed for a split second – and then he was Harriman again: calm, controlled and authoritarian. Tom thought he had imagined it and glanced at Naina and Tiny, but they seemed unaware of any change.

Harriman's words jarred him back to reality. 'It means the planet's orbit around the sun has been changed by the impact. We are still unsure by how much.'

'So what hit us?'

'Phobos.'

'The *moon* Phobos?'

Harriman nodded. 'Phobos struck the Pavonis Mons in equatorial region. Its impact released the volcanic pressure beneath the surface.'

Tiny shifted uneasily in his seat. 'So what's the damage – to the planet, I mean?'

Harriman continued. 'Quantities of sub-surface ice were vaporised by the impact, and deeper ice stores were super-heated by volcanic activity.' He paused. 'The planet has been deep frozen for so long that the meeting between fire and ice has been devastating.' He sat for a moment. 'And now, for the first time in billions of years, Mars has liquid water.'

Naina nodded. 'The cave where we sat out the worst of the

storm turned out to be part of an ancient water course. We were lucky to escape.'

Harriman cast a lingering stare towards Tom and he felt as though he were being observed from the inside out. He squirmed under the attention. A flash of memory, a moment of recollection like insect legs scurrying across his mind caused him to shiver, and words echoed inside his head. *Some of you have been luckier than others.*

Tom looked up, thrust the intrusion from his mind, and stared hard into Harriman's eyes. He sensed nothing, and for a moment his eyes grew heavy.

Harriman's voice droned and Tom's consciousness swam as though his head had been struck. He opened his eyes to a kaleidoscope of colour which filled his vision, and Tom felt his body swept along as motion sickness took over. He squeezed his eyes shut and breathed deeply as he began to count, hoping he could quell the nauseous sensation in the pit of his stomach, and then everything stopped.

Tom found himself in a heap, and drank in the coolness of the floor beneath him. It felt soothing as he struggled to settle his stomach and still his mind, and after a number of deep breaths was finally able to open his eyes.

He was startled to find himself in a large room. Book lined shelves towered above him and he climbed warily to his feet. As he wandered down dark avenues a familiar voice, binding him to his past like a whisper out of time, filled his head. He was unsure whether it was a dream, or a ghost of something more.

Memories filled his head as he took in the sights around him. They were recognizable, their presence familiar, and for a moment he sank into the past.

Tom felt his head spin, the movement unexpected, and found himself opposite Harriman once more. He sunk forward and rubbed at his face while Harriman's voice droned.

Was that real? Was I actually there, or was it just another illusion? The days of his youth were long gone, his childhood no more than a memory. Surely it couldn't have happened – could it?

Tom climbed wearily to his feet and wandered to the back of the room. He struggled to pull himself from the moment, his body and mind so very, very tired.

Tiny pushed his chair back, his elbows on his knees as his fingers rubbed a tension spot at the back of his neck. He considered the enormity of Harriman's disclosure as he stumbled through a myriad of questions, his thoughts wrapped around themselves like the body of a snake which squeezed and restricted his grasp of events.

Change of orbit – geological and atmospheric activity – surface movement - loss of contact – Earth.

'Which direction?'

'Pardon?' Tiny's question took Harriman by surprise. He hadn't expected it.

'Which direction are we falling - sunward?' Tiny already knew the answer, but needed clarification. The question was important: falling towards the sun would cause the planet to continue to heat, but falling away had even more serious considerations.

'Sunward, but gradually.'

Tiny nodded and sucked at his top lip. Either way it didn't really make a difference; heat up or freeze, neither option was ideal, but at least falling towards the Sun was falling closer towards Earth. NASA may be able to launch a ship, may be able to direct something their way as a lifeline, but it would be a one shot mission; a final act of desperation. Tiny shook his head; it didn't look good.

'So what about conditions on the surface? What are we up against?' Always the scientist, Naina was looking beyond the short-term problems.

Harriman placed his mug to one side and thumbed a switch before interlacing his fingers. A 3D globe sprung into life before them, pulsing discs indicating multiple points of volcanic activity. 'Phobos struck here, on the western quarter.' He pointed at the location of the strike. 'The impact was deeply wounding. It dug deep into the planet and created a surge of intense volcanic activity which broke through the surface of the planet here.' He pointed to an area on the western fringe of the planet. It bordered the giant Valles Marineris rift valley with a series of volcanoes. 'And here.' He indicated a flat plain to the north. 'Unfortunately, we don't know enough about the damage inflicted to predict further developments.'

'But the planet is being heated from the inside?' Naina was studying the globe carefully.

'It is, but the changes are so dramatic that anything we once knew is now irrelevant.'

Tom returned to the conversation. 'But you must have a means of escape - after all, this is pretty advanced stuff.' He indicated the vehicle around them. 'Whoever put you here believes you are valuable. There's been too much money spent on all this to lose you.'

Harriman hesitated. 'Our ship is...damaged.'

'Beyond repair?' Tiny folded his arms and sat back, his head angled slightly to one side. He was fishing, and Harriman knew it.

'Possibly.' Harriman returned Tiny's gaze.

Tiny's voice took on a no-nonsense edge; he was not in the mood for misinformation. 'Who sent you, who funded all this? You're not regular space industry, that's obvious. If we're stuck here, then I think you should open up. After all, we may be here for the rest of our lives...however short that may be.'

Harriman hardened. He stood and pulled his shirt sleeves down under his tunic cuffs, his manner brusque and business like. 'As I said earlier, you will be told what you need to know. As of this moment, that's precisely what you have been told.'

A shadow invaded Tom's vision. It passed through his mind like a silent whisper. *Ask no more questions.* But Tom wasn't prepared to listen to the voice. Something had drawn him towards Mars like a bee to an open flower, its secrets a delicate treasure hidden deep within. It was as if the planet had sensed his presence and held out a welcoming hand, but now its secrets had begun to close in on themselves, holding him here like an insect in a trap.

Tom's life was entwined with the visions of an early Mars which no-one had ever witnessed. He felt as though he were a part of something much larger, and sensed his role was not yet over.

But what had he been sent here to do?

Tom rounded the table and approached Harriman before he realised he had even done it. 'How long have you *really* been here?' he said. 'How long, and why?'

Harriman didn't answer, but his expression said all Tom needed to know.

Longer than you can possibly imagine.

CHAPTER 43

For the next week the crew was confined to specific areas of the vehicle, and allowed limited computer access. Tiny worked relentlessly to crack the security codes on his workstation, but after three days he gave up in disgust.

There was little else to do except wander between the galley and their quarters, and after a while Tom found solitude in his bunk, drifting between his own thoughts and tortured sleep. Tiny and Naina sensed Tom needed time alone and gave him the space he so obviously craved.

He roused at a knock, the door to his quarters opening just enough for Naina to peep through. 'You feel like company?' she asked. Tom nodded and she stepped in. Tiny followed, and an uncomfortable look passed between them.

'Listen, mate, Naina and I have been talking.' Tom sat up and stretched. Something clicked in his back and he flinched. Tiny carried on. 'We think it's about time you filled us in on the background to...' He didn't know quite how to address it. '...all this.'

Tom climbed wearily to his feet and peeled off the upper part of his jumpsuit. It hung around his waist as he reached into his locker.

Naina spoke gently. 'We think you owe us the truth.'

Tom sighed. 'You're right, I do.' He stripped off and pulled on a clean undershirt, then crossed the floor to his bunk. He sat down slowly and faced his friends. Time dragged as he pursed his lips, but neither Tiny nor Naina pressed him further. Finally, he looked up.

'You have to understand I was a normal kid. I played the games the other kids played and watched the same movies.' A slight smile crossed his face. 'I even had an annoying sister like

136

my other mates, but I hated school and didn't really apply myself. The teachers were always on at me about my attitude, but I didn't care.'

Tom's eyes were downcast as he slipped back into memory. 'Basically, I'd switched off. It took something major to switch me back on again.'

He clicked his tongue absently and then raised his eyes. 'Abi wasn't that bad, though. She was younger and an irritation, but, when we moved house, life was suddenly different. I was in a world totally opposite to the one I'd been used to, and at first I took to it badly. Abi and I only had each other for company and it took a while until we become friends.' He dropped his eyes to stare at the floor, his sister's face swimming before him, her long blond hair and sharp blue eyes causing a smile to cross his face. They were his abiding memory of his sister - a woman he had come to love dearly, and a woman he would probably never see again.

It took a few seconds for the sadness to pass. When it did his voice was filled with contentment. 'Living in the countryside wasn't as bad as I'd first thought, and we quickly grew to love it.' He smiled at the memory. 'The fresh air and the open spaces were the perfect contrast after the suburbs of Manchester. I suppose you could say the hills were our saviour.'

He paused, unsure how to begin the next part of the story. He chewed his bottom lip as he sat wrapped in the demons of his past.

Slowly, he explained about Danny Forbes, his Father's old school friend, and how he had appeared suddenly at their door; how he had brought an ordeal that had terrified the whole family with its lights and shadows as the An'Tsari had surrounded them in the darkness. The agonising vibrations and blinding lights had terrified them all, and Tom's world had changed forever.

Although the family's collective memory of the events had been erased by the alien presence, peeled away like layers of dead skin, Tom had been left untouched, and it had frightened him.

Neither Tiny nor Naina spoke. They listened in rapt attention as Tom relived his past. His recount of the UFO encounter stilled them, and they watched as the fear played itself across his face. It was not a pleasant thing to watch.

Tom fell into silence for a while, his breathing heavy and his eyes misted with tears as he remembered the terror he had once felt. After much soul searching, he picked up his story again.

For years he had lived in fear of every dark night, every sound in the darkness, but after a time had learnt to deal with it. He had found strength to block out the fears and the truth, like closing a lid on an unwanted gift, and had stored the boxes deep within his consciousness. As time passed they were buried, hidden away beneath good memories and happy times, and he had learned to enjoy life again. And then, unexpectedly, his perception of the world had begun to change.

He had read everything he could lay his hands on. At first he had read the novels which stocked the bookshelves of his home, and had then progressed to the more academic texts his father kept in the dusty loft. He had become fascinated not just by how things worked, but *why* they worked. He had devoured scientific books and magazines in great numbers, and his school work had changed dramatically as a result.

At first his teachers thought he must be cheating, copying work from internet sites and passing it off as his own, but as the new Tom Richards unfolded before their eyes, they found him to be an honest and hardworking student.

'It was the presence I had buried away, but it resurfaced, and this time it was different. It held me together,' Tom said. 'I drew strength from it, although it was never there when I consciously listened for it. It only appeared as I drifted towards sleep, and I often thought I'd imagined it.

He paused again. 'I felt differently about myself, and came to believe I was destined to do something important, yet I had no idea what.'

Tom straightened and folded his arms, his manner serious. 'I know now that my life has been channelled, and the sole reason I'm on Mars is because of that single event in my childhood. That night terrified me and it still terrifies me to this day. At this moment I feel as though I belong on Mars. On some strange subconscious level, I'm part of it.' He paused, unsure what to say next. 'I suppose you could liken it to those cases of twins who don't feel whole when they're apart from one another.'

'Well, after what happened on the surface I think it's safe to say you do have some kind of connection, but why didn't you tell us this before? We've known each other a long time...' Naina's voice was soft, her tone slightly hurt.

Tom smiled. 'I suppose it was all too...personal.'

Tiny changed the direction of the conversation. 'I need to ask you what happened outside - in the storm.' The question had burned inside Tiny for so long, it almost burst its way out. 'Was it that presence that kept you alive, or was it something else?'

'It was him.'

'Who?' Tiny and Naina both sat forward.

'I only knew him as Mr. Lampard.' Tom's memory of the old man was his wild unkempt hair and piercing black eyes, but after the poor start to their friendship, Mr. Lampard had become tantalisingly friendly, so much so, that part of Tom had been deeply saddened when the old man had disappeared. It was after Tom and Mr. Lampard had sat together in the library that the librarian had failed to appear for work. In the weeks that followed, Mr. Lampard had been officially classed as a missing person, and had never been found.

The dream-time conversation which followed the An'Tsari encounter had taken many months before it had awakened inside Tom's conscious mind. He had become aware of Mr. Lampard in his dreams, and had been initially frightened by the old man's presence, but over time he had come to understand that he meant no harm.

But he told me the An'Tsari were dying, thought Tom. *Why did he lie to me?*

He was jolted back to reality by Tiny's question. 'Who was he?'

Tom felt uneasy discussing the old man's origin, and shuffled as he weighed up how to proceed. *What's to hide?* he thought at last. *They know more than anyone else, so why hide the truth?* He took a deep breath. 'He was one of the An'Tsari. The Seeders.'

'The *what?*' Tiny was stunned. Naina folded her arms and raised her eyebrows.

'The An'Tsari. They seeded the universe.'

'Seeded it? From where?'

'From their own DNA, and we in turn are seeded from them.'

Tiny rubbed his fingers through his short hair and scrubbed at his growth of beard. 'This just gets better,' he said. He huffed as he looked at Naina. 'You couldn't write this stuff.'

Naina shushed him. 'So what happened… out there?' She indicated beyond the vehicle.

It was the part Tom was the least sure about. 'I went somewhere. Mr Lampard showed me the most wonderful things.'

'Like what?'

Tom smiled. 'This planet. Four billion years ago.'

'Four *billion?*' Tiny sat up.

'What did you see?' Naina's voice was quiet and trembling. 'What did you find?'

'Life.' Tom paused and took a deep breath. 'There was life here before it ever evolved on Earth. You see, Earth was their second try.'

The conversation went round and round, Tom explaining the visions he had seen, the wonders of a world long gone. Finally he drew away from the subject.

Tiny wandered over to the viewport and stared into the darkness, but Naina pulled them back together. 'So what happened next? When you were growing up, I mean.'

Tom clicked his tongue while he thought. 'I met Annie shortly after my encounter with the An'Tsari,' he said. 'She was new to my school when we returned after the summer break.' His voice was little more than a whisper. 'She was special.'

Naina sensed immediately that Annie had been more than a friend, and knew it was going to be a hard story to tell.

'Who was she?'

Tom seemed shrunken, smaller somehow as he remembered. 'Annie Hope. Her name was Annie Hope.' He paused briefly. 'I was nearly eleven when she joined my school, but Annie made an impression on me straight away. Up until that point I'd never been interested in girls, and I'd gone back to school that autumn with a much more focused approach – 'New and Improved,' my teacher had called me – but from the moment she walked in I knew she was someone special.'

'Annie was friendly from the outset, and within a few days it was as though she'd always been there. She brought something to the class that changed it.'

'It, or you?' Naina smiled.

'Both, I guess.'

'What do you mean?' Naina's tone was gentle.

'I'd gone back to school with a different agenda: I'd become a real bookworm, but I'd done it in secret. The mates I'd hung around with weren't interested in space and UFOs and all that stuff, so at the start of the year I kept my fascinations to myself. It was my little secret.' Tom moved himself to the seat by the computer terminal. 'There was no-one I could tell about my experience - even my parents didn't remember any of it.' Exasperation was evident as he spoke. 'How could I tell my friends?' He shook his head, his nose wrinkled as though at a bad smell. 'I couldn't tell them anything.'

'I take it Annie played some important part in all this?' Tiny's question caught Tom unexpectedly. After Naina's calming voice, his friend's tone was sudden, like a jolt of electricity.

Tom's eyes held an expression of hurt and his body seemed to grow even smaller, everything about him sorrowful. 'Yes, she did,' he said, his voice fading as he lost himself in his memories. He avoided all eye contact as he spoke. 'Annie Hope was a beautiful person, in every sense of the word. She was intelligent and thoughtful, kind and considerate, and there was something about her which was captivating from the first moment I saw her.'

Tiny laughed. 'First love, eh, mate?' He thought he knew everything there was to know about Tom. They'd been the best of friends for over twenty years, ever since the Return to the Moon and subsequent Mars Missions had been first announced, but this was something new; it was a part of Tom's life his friend had chosen not to share until now.

Tom spoke quietly. 'I suppose you could say she was.' He nodded as he spoke. 'I loved it when she was in the room; I worked better and I felt as though she was pushing me onwards, encouraging me to do better. And then Mr Grendal sat her next to me. I remember she gave me a timid smile, and that was it. I felt as though her being there was the key to everything, and from that moment on I knuckled down: I worked harder than I'd ever worked in my whole life. Everything I did just seemed to make sense.'

'What do you mean?'

Tom ran his tongue over his lips before continuing. 'You know how some of the things you learn at school don't seem to make sense on their own? How history and geography and science can all be interesting as individual subjects, but sometimes there seems to be no connection between them, no purpose in them being taught?'

Tiny nodded, remembering his own school days. 'Tell me about it.'

'I mean, what has poetry got to do with the formation of riverbeds, and what has the construction of the Great Pyramids got to do with musical notation? Well, it was as though the links had suddenly come alive. And not just within those subjects, but within everything. I saw connections between every subject like the gossamer threads of a spider's web. It was as though a great map was suddenly laid out before me, a vast plan comprised of interconnecting layers, and I understood everything.' He paused. 'I tried explaining it to my Dad once, but after about ten minutes he just gave up; my explanation lost him.'

'But what has this got to do with a girl?' Tiny was intrigued.

Tom cast a piercing stare, his brows knitted in sudden

irritation at Tiny's choice of words. It was something Tiny had only ever seen his friend do once before.

'Annie,' said Tom irately. 'You mean Annie.'

Tiny held up his hands in apology. 'Sorry. Yes, I mean Annie.'

Tom held his friend's gaze for a moment and then looked away. Naina smiled and leaned forwards, her voice barely above a whisper as she defused the moment. 'Tell me more about Annie.'

Tom inhaled deeply. 'She sat next to me one afternoon - we'd become quite good friends by that time - and began flicking through a small notepad on my desk. She came across a page of doodles - triangles mostly, each corner decorated with a small circle – and saw the pattern repeated across other pages inside the back cover. She asked me what it all meant.'

'What did you say?'

'I said it was nothing, just something I drew when I was bored, but she seemed intrigued, as though she saw something else in it. I told her it was nothing and put the pad away.'

'That evening my Dad shouted for me to come downstairs and there was Annie, standing inside our hallway. I felt my heart race and glanced at my Dad, not sure what he was going to say, but he just smiled and winked as he walked past. I didn't know what to do.' Tom shrugged. 'I'll admit, I was embarrassed.'

"I've brought you something,' she said. 'It's something you need to see,' and she held out a magazine.' Tom folded his arms and repositioned himself. 'I ushered her outside and we sat on the front doorstep. I didn't know what else to do.'

'What was the magazine?'

'*National Geographic*,' said Tom. It was a tatty old copy, its spine worn and cracked, its edges well thumbed and creased. The cover showed a beautiful star-filled sky with a dark shape silhouetted against it. At the bottom of the page, in white lettering, was a question:

SKY SHADOWS:
WORLDLY OR OTHERWORLDLY?

'I stared at the words, my hands shaking, and Annie took the magazine from me. She opened it, and inside were images of black triangles photographed against the night sky. Many of them were similar to images I'd seen before.'

'Annie took hold of my hand as I stared at the pictures. She spoke only three words, but they meant so much to me: 'I believe, too."

'That must have been a relief,' said Naina, 'having someone to share things with.' Tom didn't respond, the memories hard to relive. He paused and rubbed his hands together while he composed himself, the hardest memories yet to come.

'Annie and I became inseparable from that moment on, and over the next ten years were rarely apart. It was as though we knew each other inside out. Annie understood how I saw the world, with its connections and layers, its sprawling masses of information, and she supported me without questioning any part of it.'

Tom moved to a water dispenser and drew himself a drink, then returned to his bunk. He sipped from the cup as he collected his thoughts, then placed it on the floor by his feet. 'Abi and Annie soon became friends as well, although Abi was a few years younger.' He looked up. 'But that didn't seem to matter. We often went round together; somehow it just seemed right.'

'A triangle,' commented Naina. Tom smiled; the imagery hadn't been lost on him either.

'We were part of a wider group of friends which, funnily enough, totalled nine.'

'Three squared,' added Naina, her smile light. 'Convenient. It seems almost engineered.'

Tom laughed. 'Yeah, but we didn't think anything of it at the time. We just had a lot of friends, that's all.'

'So did you tell Annie about your experience? What did she think?'

'No. As much as I loved and trusted her, I just couldn't. She knew I was hiding some kind of secret, some shadow which I was keeping from her, but she just accepted it. I'd already decided I

144

wasn't going to tell anyone: it was my secret, no matter how deep it went.'

'So what happened? Why did it end?'

Tom's voice caught in his throat. 'It didn't; well, not as you'd expect.' He paused again and drained the cup. 'One day she just...vanished.' He looked up and his eyes showed the pain he felt. 'I mean literally vanished. Gone. Without trace.'

'Where did she go? What do you think happened?'

Tom shook his head slowly, his face blank as he spoke. His voice was distant. 'I honestly don't know.' He folded his arms as though holding himself in. 'The police searched for her, but...' he sighed. 'She's still classed as a missing person.'

'Oh, Tom, that's terrible.' Naina's eyes misted and she bit her lip. Tiny's face was pale at the disclosure, shocked that something so deeply hurtful had happened to his friend and he had known nothing about it. Naina could barely control her voice. 'What did you do?'

'I had to get on with my life. I missed her terribly – I still do – but something has niggled at the back of my mind since the day she vanished, as though I've missed something vital, as though somehow I've missed the point.'

There was a long silence in the room. When Tom spoke his revelation was shocking.

'Annie's disappearance was one of the two great losses in my life.'

'What was the other?'

Tom took a breath and let it go slowly. 'The death of my mother.'

CHAPTER 44

'When my Mum died I just didn't know what to do: I mean, who would? When you're thirteen it's the last thing you think is ever going to happen. It's an unreal possibility. Your world is so full of the moment, and you're always looking forward to the next big thing. I know I was.'

Naina spoke gently, her words carefully spoken so as not to jar the memory Tom was reliving. 'How did your mother die?'

Tom screwed the paper cup into a ball and threw it towards the bin. It struck the edge and bounced. Finally, he looked up.

'Mum and I were on the way back from Whitby. A car careered out of the Blakey junction without stopping and caught us broadside. Mum saw it coming and tried to swerve, but there was nowhere to go. I thought for a moment we were going to make it, but we clipped the front of the other car and then rolled. I don't remember much else.' He gave a shuddering breath and coughed. 'When I was pulled from the wreckage the car was nearly flat.' He swallowed. 'Mum died instantly.'

'Oh, my...' Naina slid onto the bunk beside him and slipped

her arm around Tom's waist. Tiny huffed out a big breath.

'How badly were you injured?'

'Tom's expression was blank. 'That's the thing – I was totally unhurt, except for a single speck of blood on my left arm where I cut myself climbing out of the wreckage. It was as though the car had crumpled around me – everywhere except where I'd been sitting. The police couldn't believe anyone had survived an accident like that.'

Tiny dragged his chair closer to the bunk and placed a hand on his friend's shoulder. 'Oh, man. Why didn't you tell me this before?' He didn't know what else to say.

Tom looked up and smiled, then continued. 'I thought I'd just been lucky, but I realised afterwards that something had happened in the crash, something which I've never been able to understand. Until now.'

Naina took hold of Tom's hand and squeezed it gently. She hugged him and moved away.

'Annie helped us all, but it took me a long time to accept that I'd lived and my mum had died.

'I don't know how you ever got over it. I don't think I would.' Tiny's face showed the shock he felt.

'It was about three years until we found ourselves in some kind of normal life again, although Dad has never been the same person since. Annie and I became stronger because of it, and our circle of friends widened as we left school, but while most of our other friends dated and broke up the way people do, we never faltered.'

'Didn't Annie think it was uncanny that you'd walked away from the accident unharmed? You must have talked about it.'

'We did, but she was just so glad I was still alive.' He smiled, the expression weak. 'She had always been close with Mum, but if she had lost us both...' Tom didn't need to finish.

When he continued, the subject had a different edge to it. 'No matter how many times I ran it through my mind, I had the strangest feeling I was being watched, somehow protected from anything that could hurt me. It was as though I hadn't been *allowed* to die that day.' He glanced between Tiny and Naina, expecting a reaction.

'And you think...' Tiny understood the insinuation, but it was too grand a possibility to grasp.

Tom nodded. 'And there was something else; I felt myself drawn to all kinds of experiences, as though my life was taking on a new direction.' He sat up. 'Sure, I was surrounded by good friends who were there for me through everything, offering support when I needed it, but I also found comfort in my studies. And you know, the strangest thing was that everywhere I went I found references to this planet – to Mars – as if it had some kind of hold over me.' Tom's expression changed, a satisfied smile warming his eyes. 'I knew that someday I would step foot here.'

'Well, you certainly did that,' said Tiny. His broad smile matched Tom's and they grinned at each other, but Tom's smile soon faded and his mood darkened.

'There was another experience when I was fourteen years old which convinced me, once and for all, that the car crash had not been a fluke.'

Tiny moved over to the water dispenser and poured himself a drink. When he returned, Tom picked up his thread.

'I'd just celebrated my sixteenth birthday. It was January and we'd had a really cold winter that year. It had snowed from mid-December until just after Christmas Day, when a big freeze set in. Temperatures dropped as low as minus ten for about a week – maybe even colder, I don't quite remember - and everything was frozen solid. I'd never seen anything like it.'

Tom took a moment to think before picking up the story. 'I remember arranging to meet with the gang by the oak tree in the village, but only a few turned up. We'd had this idea to go poly-bagging, you see - '

'Polly-bagging?' Tiny was confused.

Tom grinned as he explained. 'Sledging on thick polythene bags. It's faster than using a sledge, and great fun, but believe me, it hurts!' He grinned. 'You'd love it. Anyway, we ended up by the pond and stupidly began daring each other to walk out on the ice. It was frozen in great plates that wouldn't break no matter how hard we tried. So, egged on by the stupidity of youth, we tested it further away from the bank.'

Naina rolled her eyes and Tom held his hands up in supplication. 'Yes, okay. I know it was crazy, but we've all done daft things we shouldn't. Most times we're lucky,' he pulled a strangled expression and crossed his eyes, 'but on that occasion my luck ran out. Even though both Abi and Annie pleaded with me not to, I walked further out than anyone had dared to go. I felt I was invincible, as though I'd be safe no matter what. 'The exuberance of youth', my grandad had always called it.'

'And let me guess – you fell in.' Tiny laughed at the obvious outcome and Tom nodded. 'The last thing I remember before I fell in was Annie's face, her eyes full of worry as she pleaded with me to come back off the ice. And then it gave way. The water was deeper than any of us knew and I went right under.' Tom clicked his fingers. 'It was as quick as that.' He shivered as the icy coldness covered his body once again, its deathly fingers searching their way inside his soul. 'No matter how I tried, I couldn't haul myself up. My boots filled with water and my coat became heavy. I sunk quickly and started to drown.'

Tom subconsciously folded his arms as though to keep his own body heat in. 'I remember seeing the surface just above my head, but couldn't pull myself up. The edge of the ice hole broke away every time I grasped at it, and the more I struggled to gain a grip, the deeper I sunk.'

Tom coughed. He choked again, as he had many times in his dreams, and his face took on an expression Tiny couldn't place. It was as though he were looking inward, but seeing something he did not understand. As he remembered, his voice fell to hardly more than a whisper. 'I saw someone that day.'

'Who?'

Tom shrugged. 'I'm not sure. I could hear a voice telling me I was going to be all right, telling me I had to relax and let things take their course. In hindsight it was probably just my mind playing tricks, convincing me to just accept the inevitable, the way it does when people drown.' Tom's voice was desperate. 'But deep down, beyond all logic, I know it was something more.'

The past weighed heavily. 'I could hear a voice inside my head and its strength buoyed me up. I swear, I could physically feel hands lifting me.' He fell silent again. 'And there was a light, a physical light in the water around me. It was as though there were a figure within it and the liquid receded, providing me with a space to breathe. I felt warm and enveloped.'

'That sounds like hypothermia setting in. When the brain becomes too cold it convinces itself that the body is warm.' Tiny was matter of fact. 'You know that.'

Tom gave a strange tilt of the head as though he were not convinced. 'I know, but there was something else. The ice which had been so hard earlier became soft and easy to break.'

'That was your mind playing tricks on you; it had to be. A sudden change in temperature and oxygen starvation causes hallucinations.' Tiny spoke the words Tom already knew, but they didn't feel right. He knew the truth was very different; he knew that it had been Annie.

'I know. But honestly, something happened.'

Tiny changed the subject. 'How did you get out?'

'William Blakeley and Michael Dennis found a spot in the ice, a place where the ice had suddenly turned to slush. They said it just fell apart as they waded out, but by the time they grabbed me, I'd been underwater for nearly ten minutes and should have been dead. They tried to clear my lungs of water, but it didn't make a difference.'

Tom coughed. 'I was airlifted out by the Air Ambulance, but by the time the helicopter arrived I'd been unconscious for over twenty-five minutes. The paramedics who airlifted me out couldn't find a pulse, but on the way to hospital my heart suddenly started beating again, as though it had been shocked.' Tom glanced at Tiny briefly. 'They said it was the most unbelievable thing they'd ever witnessed.'

'What else do you remember?' asked Naina

Tom considered his words as though a wrong choice would change the whole meaning of the conversation. 'I was aware of everything going on above the ice and around me in the water. I was also aware of something inside.'

'Inside *you?*'

'I knew that I should have been dead, but there was a sensation of intense warmth, a burning which radiated from the inside out. Apparently my body temperature actually increased, my organs working to combat the intense cold, and I knew it was Annie. I could sense her presence as I floundered under the ice. I could even smell her and feel her touch on my skin. I knew she was alongside me, inside me, but there was someone else as well.' Tom paused and studied his fingers as they fumbled absent-mindedly. 'At the time I didn't know who it was, but the presence had a familiarity; a feeling.' He sighed. 'Looking back now, especially after my recent experiences, I knew who it was.'

Tiny interrupted Tom's thinking. 'Let me guess...'

'Yes, it was Mr. Lampard.'

The computer beeped, and the tension of the moment was broken. Tom looked up, glad of the interruption, and tapped at the screen.

A circular symbol flashed against the dark background. As Tom touched it, the symbol uncoiled to reveal a single line of glowing text which grabbed his interest immediately. Tiny dragged his chair closer to the workstation but Naina didn't move. She shivered with the after effects of Tom's story, ice running through her veins as her imagination played his story over and over again. She remained seated while Tom read the message aloud.

`Keep watch, for shadows hide many truths.`

The message was anonymous. Tom tapped out a return message on the screen and clicked *Send*.

`Shadows?`

The reply was swift.

```
You must be vigilant. You are being watched.
```

Tiny leaned over Tom's shoulder. 'Tell me something we don't know.' He drummed his fingers on the worktop as he studied the additional data on the screen's sidebar. 'There's no sender location – look.' He pointed to a line of zero's that usually carried a four-digit code. When Tim, Naina and he had communicated with each other from their own workstations, their messages had been prefixed with a four-digit sender code, but here there was nothing.

Tom's face was etched with a frown. He typed urgently.

```
Being watched, by whom?
```

The wait was longer this time.

```
I cannot say, but you must be prepared.
```

'Prepared? What's that supposed to mean?' Tiny angled the screen towards him took and took over.

```
For what?
```

The reply gave no hint.

```
Be prepared.
```

Naina settled herself between the two men. The monitor's brightness reflected across her face and she gave a weak smile as they sat.

Tiny changed the direction of questioning. 'Let's try this.'

```
Who are you?
```

The answer was no more than they had expected.

> You do not need to know,
> but must be aware that
> things are not as they seem.

Tom frowned. *Was anything as it seemed anymore?* He reached for the screen and typed.

> What must I watch for?

Tom barely had time to sit back before the reply appeared:

> The truth.

Tom stared at the message, his mind a whirl of possibilities as the computer waited for his next words.

'Well it looks as if we have someone on our side,' he said, his lips pursed in thought.

'Here, let me.' Naina reached for the screen and tapped at its glowing keyboard.

> Do you know the truth?

The response was almost instantaneous.

> The truth is not always as one
> would wish it to be.

Naina typed again.

> Tell me more.

A long pause, then a revealing answer.

> The reason we are here.

She typed quickly.

Who are you?

The cursor flashed repeatedly, but there were no further messages.

CHAPTER 45

Tom replayed the messages, searching for something, some missed clue, but drew a blank.

'We have to find out more about the organisation who created this,' said Tiny, indicating their surroundings. 'We need to know whom we're playing with. They're far too secretive.'

'I've already told you, it's a Black Project. There's no other explanation.' Tom stared out of the view port as dawn lit the landscape. Great oceans of red-stained water lay before them; it rolled outwards in undulating waves as the treads of the vehicle churned through it.

Tiny stuffed his hands into his pockets and frowned at the floor, his thoughts distant. 'There's something about Harriman that doesn't ring true,' he said. 'It's nothing to do with his secretive nature - that's the Commander in him, military or not.'

'Well, I think I'm a pretty good judge of character,' said Naina. 'I can usually work people out fairly early on, but you're right: Harriman doesn't fit. He's cold, and there's something unnatural in his attitude. He just doesn't belong.'

Tom nodded. 'But if someone in this bucket of bolts is willing to tip us off about being watched, they must be pretty high up.' He folded his arms and leaned his back against the view port. 'Not everyone has the Commander's ear, we know that.'

'But why? Are we in danger?'

Tom shook his head. 'I don't understand: why threaten us if we have nowhere to go and no-one to tell? We're stuck here. What harm can we possibly do? It doesn't make any sense.'

Tiny faced his friends. 'Well, I think it's time we earned our wages, don't you? We need to find some answers.'

'Unless you've forgotten, we have a guard on the door,' said Naina, 'and I'll bet he has no intention of letting us explore.' She cast a quick glance at Tiny and recognised a twinkle in his eye. She laughed as she told him off. 'Oh no,' she said. 'You're not...'

'Just leave him to me,' said Tiny, and with a wink he stepped away from the window.

CHAPTER 46

Throughout the night the vehicle had crawled steadily from the boggy lowlands, until, shortly before sunrise, it had come to rest atop a flat hilltop. The Martian night, only slightly longer than that of Earth, had passed with a final barrage of squalls; the sky had moved quickly through bands of changing colour and a large star had hauled itself above the horizon. But this had been a new dawn, and the star had quickly risen higher into the early morning sky than it had for billions of years.

Pink sunlight had danced across oceans of tiny wavelets, their crests shining in the dawn as they flickered and sparkled like a carpet of fallen stars. Long shadows had rolled forwards, blood red against the surrounding landscape as rivers of water, thick with stony silt and the last remnants of ice, dominated the landscape.

Bathed in morning sunlight, the vehicle had looked down upon a landscape cleansed of dust and debris to reveal a network of intricate patterns. Sprawled across the landscape, their existence finally revealed after four and a half billion years in hiding, their power would prove to be greater than anything the human race could ever have imagined.

CHAPTER 47

As soon as the hatch opened, Tiny bulldozed his way out. He caught the guard in the middle of the back and slammed him against the far wall. Dazed by the impact, the guard rose quickly to his knees, ready to fight, but Tiny's first punch sent him reeling. A succession of iron-hard blows followed, and the guard was forced down once more. He did not remain conscious for long.

Tiny climbed to his feet and hauled the guard into Tom's quarters. He had tried to make as little noise as possible, but Naina was concerned the sounds of struggle had carried. She checked the corridor nervously and then closed the hatch.

'What is it with men?' she grumbled. 'You're only happy when you're flexing your muscles. Did you *have* to make that much noise?'

'Well, you know how it is – I never like to pass up a challenge.' Tiny winked and turned his attention to the guard's uniform. 'Great - he's about my size. That should make this easier.'

Tom beckoned to Naina. 'Keep your ear to the door while we get his uniform off - if someone misses this guy we're sunk.' She nodded and placed her ear against the hatch while Tiny unzipped the guard's jumpsuit.

'Have you thought this through properly? We're not going to have long…'

'It'll be okay. Trust me.' Tiny smiled as he pulled the jumpsuit free and pushed his own feet into the legs. 'But this guy won't be out for long, so we'll have to make it quick.'

Naina gestured as she heard footsteps, their sound dull on the heavy deck plates of the corridor. They stepped confidently closer, their pace slowing as they approached the hatch, and stopped outside.

Tiny flattened himself against the bulkhead and gestured for Naina to step away. If someone opened the hatch, he didn't want Naina to be in the way. The last thing they needed was for one of them to be injured.

The booted feet shuffled beyond the hatch and Tom felt a wave of dizziness. The sensation was tinged with an odour he could not place, and he shook his head to clear it. Finally, as the boots moved away, Tiny cracked open the hatch. He peered into the corridor but found it silent and empty. 'That was close,' he said. He stepped back inside and pulled the jumpsuit over his shoulders as Tom passed him the blue cap. He crammed it on and pulled the brim low over his eyes.

'How do I look?' He smiled his cheekiest grin.

Naina adjusted his collar and pinched his cheek. 'Like a little boy playing at soldiers,' she said. 'You're enjoying this, aren't you?'

As they crept along the deserted corridor, Tiny stopped to read an identification plate. 'Records,' he said. 'This is where we want to be.' He pulled himself up to his full height and dipped his head slightly as he adjusted his cap. It cast a shadow over his eyes and concealed his features enough to provide a few seconds' advantage.

The hatch opened with a soft *clunk* and he stepped through into a darkened room. A bank of monitors lined the far wall, their screens lit with a range of images, but the room was deserted. He opened the hatch wide. 'Empty,' he said, and Tom and Naina shuffled in behind. 'Right, let's find out who these guys are. But quickly.'

A circular crest stared at Tom from the main VDU screen. It was similar to that emblazoned on the jumpsuit Tiny wore, but with the addition of twelve numbered circles overlaid upon its outer ring. A single word was glowed across its centre:

MAJESTIC

Interesting, thought Tom. *Could it really be them, after all this time?* He pressed his index finger to the first small circle and it spun outwards. An image appeared within it, but the text was too small to read. He tapped experimentally and the box expanded quickly to fill the lower half of the screen.

HARRIMAN, WILLIAM PAUL - DESIGNATION:MJ01
BORN AUGUST 12TH 1797, GREEN RIVER, WYOMING, USA.

Tom leaned forward and studied the text. 'Look at this – look at Harriman's date of birth…'

Naina moved to the console and made a quick mental calculation. 'But that would make him over two hundred and fifty years old. That's impossible!' she said. 'He can't be older than fifty at most.'

Tom indicated the screen. 'Well, that's what it says here.'

CAREER:
UNITED STATES AIR FORCE: 1930-1945

COMMANDER; INTELLIGENCE DIVISION
SPECIAL OPERATIONS RESEARCH AND DEVELOPMENT -
LEVEL 1 CLEARANCE

Tom turned back to the screen. 'Level 1 clearance. That sounds interesting.' He folded his arms. 'I bet he knows a thing or two.'

'About what? Tiny was curious, but Tom didn't answer; his attention was focused on the screen as other data scrolled across it.

WHITEHOUSE COMMITTEE ON TOP SECRET DEVELOPMENT
PROJECTS; 1945 – 1947; LEVEL ALPHA 1 CLEARANCE

PROJECT MAJESTIC; DIRECTOR, 1947 TO PRESENT

Tom clicked his tongue. 'MAJESTIC. Well, what do you know...?'

Naina raised her eyebrows, confusion written across her face, but Tiny was more informed. 'I've heard of them,' he said, 'but I can't say I know much about who they were.'

Tom explained. 'MAJESTIC was rumoured to be a covert organisation commissioned by President Truman after the Roswell crash in 1947. Its existence was never made public, and even less was known about its purpose. But this...' He paused. 'MAJESTIC was supposedly disbanded sometime in the 1960s.' He faced the screen again. 'They were tasked with covering up alien activities on Earth and retrieving technology from crashed spacecraft. They answered only to Truman, their existence nothing more than a rumour.'

'But the rumour took on a life of its own,' added Tiny. 'Much like an urban myth.'

Naina was confused. 'How do you know all this? If they don't exist...'

Tom smiled sheepishly. 'I was interested in all of this as a boy. Let's just say I had a personal interest - which I indulged.'

'Well carry on digging,' said Naina, 'but be quick – we're running out of time.'

Tom grunted and leaned over the screen again.

PROJECTS INSTIGATED:

PROJECT REDLIGHT; 1947 – 1953
RECOVERY OF CRASHED ALIEN CRAFT/OCCUPANTS

PROJECT AQUARIUS; 1953 - 1958
COLLECTION OF EXTRATERRESTRIAL SCIENTIFIC, TECHNICAL, MEDICAL AND INTELLIGENCE DATA

PROJECT SIGN; 1958 – 1962
EVALUATION OF HUMAN - ALIEN TREATY AND THREAT TO PLANET EARTH

PROJECT NEW WORLD; 1962 TO PRESENT
MAJESTIC RELOCATION, TECHNOLOGICAL DEVELOPMENT AND ANALYSIS OF EARTH - MARS LINKS

"MAJESTIC RELOCATION': Well, that sounds straight forward. If they were officially disbanded in the 1960s and came here to hide, that would explain a lot.' He paused as he re-read Harriman's résumé. 'But this is the bit that interests me,' he said. "PROJECT NEW WORLD.' It has quite a ring to it, don't you think?'

'It certainly throws new light on everything you've told us. If the An'Tsari initially attempted to seed Mars as you said, then this planet has meaning for them.'

Tom's lips formed a thin line as he considered the facts he had just read. He nodded, but Naina urged him on and he turned back to the screen. He flicked through the other names on the crew list, but none caught his attention. Then, as he scrolled further down, new icons appeared. 'What's this?'

He selected one and tapped it. The file piqued his interest immediately:

OPERATIONS FILE — PROGRESS RECORDS.

Naina hung over Tom's shoulder as he worked. 'What is it?'

He ferreted through a series of screens, most of the data no more than number-letter combinations. 'It looks like co-ordinates of some kind,' he said. He whistled through his teeth as a series of complex calculations scrolled before him, and then worked deeper into the file. 'Now *this* looks more like it.'

HISTORICAL ARCHIVES

'Open it,' Naina whispered. He touched the words and images flowed quickly before him. Each dissolved into the next, and Tom slid his finger over an illuminated strip against the edge of the screen. Somehow, he knew it was the right thing to do.

The images slowed to reveal linear patterns, their appearances interwoven as though etched onto a textured surface, and Tom frowned. Something about them seemed familiar, but he couldn't decide what.

He flicked through other images, stopping as a pattern of concentric swirls and an interconnecting triple band filled the screen, and instructed the computer to zoom out. The image revealed itself as part of a more complex design, yet still the image's relevance eluded him.

The view widened further to reveal an abundance of detail, each intricate pattern superimposed with interconnecting lines, but as he enlarged an image the screen suddenly went blank.

'What?' Naina tapped at the screen, her fingers searching hopelessly in an attempt to restore the images.

'Forget it. They're on to us.' Tiny pulled his friends away. 'Come on. We have to leave. Now.'

'But those images, they were…'

'I know,' said Tom. 'Crop circles.'

'But what have they got to do with all this?'

Tom dismissed her with a sweep of his hand. 'Later - we have to go.'

Tiny opened the hatch and stepped into the corridor. He ushered Naina through but Tom hung back and glanced quickly around the room. He felt sure he had been on the cusp of discovering the truth, but it had eluded him once again, the way it had eluded him for the past thirty years. Now, just as everything seemed on the verge of making sense, it had been ripped from his grasp once more.

Why were crop circles important, and why here? It didn't make sense.

Or did it?

CHAPTER 48

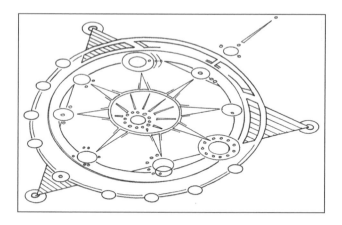

Tom had seen his first crop circle a week after his encounter with the An'Tsari. His family had taken off for a last minute holiday in Somerset, and it was while Abi and he sat eating ice-creams that something unusual first caught his attention.

A stream of people – some in walking gear, others in everyday clothes – hurried towards a narrow gap in the fence opposite. Their voices and laughter carried on the warm mid-afternoon air as they disappeared from sight.

Tom watched, intrigued. 'Where do you think they're going?'

Abi licked at her white-coated fingers as her ice-cream melted in the heat. She glanced up for a minute, shrugged, and then returned her attention to the dripping mess in her hand. 'Dunno, but they're in a hurry.'

'You fancy going to see?' Tom glanced back at his mum and dad; they sat beneath a large parasol in the beer garden of *The Old Monk*, deep in conversation, and looked as though they would be happy to stay all afternoon. Without waiting for Abi's response, Tom climbed to his feet and sauntered over. Moments later he was back, urging Abi to follow.

They strode across the field together, and Tom craned his neck to see if anything of interest lay beyond the gap in the fence. The path disappeared into a patch of trees, beyond which lay another fence where a group of people clustered.

A tall man in a light coloured T-shirt and dark blue walking trousers stood against the gap. He glanced up from the pamphlet he was reading and smiled as a lady, dressed in a flowery dress and sandals, attempted to squeeze herself between the fence posts. Her dress caught on their weathered surface and she had to coax it free before she could step through.

The man turned, his smile broad and friendly, and Tom smiled back. 'Excuse me, but where is everybody going - what's over there?' He indicated the field beyond with an outstretched hand.

The man folded his pamphlet and tucked it into a pocket. 'Over there? You mean you don't know?'

Tom shook his head. Abi licked her fingers as she finished her cone, her attention now focused on the conversation between her brother and the man.

'Why, it's the circles,' he said, his accent full of thick Somerset burr.

'The circles? What are they?'

The man laughed and Abi gave him an ice cream coated grin. He smiled back.

'They're patterns in the corn, sonny. Complicated patterns, mind you.' Tom stared blankly and the man continued, realising more explanation was needed. 'They're strange things, these circles. You see, there are no tracks to show how a vehicle got in to flatten the crop down, and no signs of how the circle was made.' The man shook his head slightly. 'It's a puzzle, I tell you, and I'm darned if I know how it's done.' He looked over the fence. 'Why don't you take a look – they're just beyond that fence.'

Tom peered through in time to see the lady in the flowered dress climb over a stile. He smirked as she teetered uncertainly, the fence wobbling under her weight, before stepping off into several sets of steadying hands and amused laughter.

'I'm going through myself. Would you like me to show you where it is?' The man slid sideways through the gap and paused on the far side. 'You coming?'

Tom was quickly through the fence. He smiled as Abi joined him. 'Yes please,' he said. 'If you don't mind.'

CHAPTER 49

They entered a field of shoulder-high corn. It swayed gently in the warm breeze, and a coarse rustle filled the air as the tall stalks rasped soothingly. A child's voice and shrill laugher wafted on the warm air, and Tom smiled. He beckoned to his sister to catch up.

'You can take any of these tracks in,' said the man. 'Go on - explore it and have some fun.' He waved, set off down a well-trodden pathway, and vanished from sight around a bend in the track.

Tom and Abi stepped into the corn together, and were soon immersed within the waving crop as the ground sloped away. The sky was almost hidden above their heads, and Tom took one branch in the path while Abi took another. The corn tickled his legs as he moved, its colour turned golden by the summer sun, and without warning he stepped out into an open space about ten metres wide. The golden-flecked corn lay flattened in an anti-clockwise direction, the wall of the circle vertical as though cut by machine.

At the centre of the open area, a single stalk of corn stood straight amongst the flattened stems, its survival in opposition to everything around it. Without realising why, Tom reached out towards it. An electrifying sensation stirred the air, and he pulled his fingers back briefly before reaching forward once again.

For a moment he lost all sense of reality. His surroundings spun, their colours blending, and a wave of nausea filled his stomach. He closed his eyes and breathed deeply, hoping to settle the sensation in the pit of his stomach, but when he opened them again he found the sky filled with shifting patterns of ochre and brown, and the landscape washed by a deep chill. It was a world governed by different rules; a vision he knew would fascinate him for the rest of his life.

He blinked, and the world vanished as swiftly as it had arrived. His own breathing was loud in the silence, but the colours filled his mind.

He became aware of a sound so faint he could easily have missed it. It drifted as if from a great distance, as though a voice were trying to communicate with him, and spoke words he did not understand. Its clarity was muffled and distorted, like an echo of itself, and Tom strained his ears to listen. It faded once, returned briefly, and then vanished.

Tom rubbed at his face and breathed deeply, the air warm but tainted by an odour, and he moved towards a narrow path in the wall of the circle. He followed it blindly as he willed the sound to return, the path forcing him to choose a new direction as it split into two. The corn pressed around him as he took the wider track, the sensation claustrophobic, until, with a final push, it parted and another space opened before him.

This space was vastly different, its corn laid in opposite bands forming a great oval. Tom stood transfixed. He remembered reading something about crop circles and their connection with UFO mythology, but hadn't taken a lot of notice. They hadn't seemed important or significant, yet now he wished he'd paid more attention. *There's so much I don't know*, he thought. *There's so much to learn.*

The atmosphere inside the oval was noticeably different to that of the circle, the air humid as it shielded him from the light wind. He crouched at the division between the stripes of corn and studied their linear edges, then moved to others. He found their edges perfect, as if drawn with a mathematical instrument, and looked up to take in the expanse of flattened corn. *How could anyone have created this?* he thought. *It doesn't seem possible.*

A whisper caused him to turn quickly, and he expected to see other figures stepping into the space, but found he was alone. *It must be someone close by*, he thought, *someone exploring another part of the field*, but the voice came again.

Every being must follow his own path.

He whipped around, startled.

Look to the future. You will know what to do.

And then there was silence.

CHAPTER 50

The crop circle faded and reality took over, but as Tom stepped through the hatch he was suddenly surrounded by static. The vehicle greyed out, its walls and low ceiling replaced by a vast cathedral-like space, and Tom found himself within an open chamber. A cluster of icicle-like columns hung high overhead, a single beam of light piercing the darkness from their centre.

He turned slowly and peered into the semi-darkness. 'Where am I?'

The reply was unexpected. 'Where you are destined to be.'

Tom wheeled around to see a figure concealed within the light, where seconds before there had been nothing. The figure's head was bowed, its features within deep shadow, and Tom had to shield his eyes against the glare.

'Who are you? Where are my friends – where are Naina and Tiny?' Tom was in need of answers.

The voice echoed around the chamber. 'Safe.'

Tom grabbed at the figure, his hands reaching out in an uncharacteristic act of aggression, but they slid through without resistance and he stumbled. He fell to his knees, caught off balance by the lack of a solid form.

'Who are you?'

The figure did not respond and Tom climbed to his feet. He brushed his hand through the light as he faced the figure. 'I know the secret you're hiding,' he said at last, 'and I know about MAJESTIC.' Tom's anger at the deceit his crew had encountered burned like fire.

The figure was confident, its manner superior. 'You think you understand, but you are dealing with something far beyond your expectations.'

'Oh, I understand enough.' Tom was fuelled by anger. 'I know you are An'Tsari, and I know why you're here - you're dying.'

The figure responded immediately, its words cynical. 'Do you honestly believe you were led here with the truth?' The words were that of a schoolyard bully riding high on his own self-confidence.

'The truth?' Tom felt his anger rise once again, the lies and deceit an unpleasant realisation, but he smiled with a confidence from deep within. It was a confidence built on knowledge. 'I understand more than you realise... '

The figure laughed. '... and I know more about you than you could ever believe.'

'More about me than...?' Tom paused to compose himself. He felt drained as his confidence ebbed away like water into dry sand, and his voice betrayed the first signs of emotion. 'Who are you?'

The figure slowly raised its head, and the beam of light illuminated its face.

It was Mr. Lampard.

CHAPTER 51

After everything he's shown me, after everything that's happened...
Tom staggered as his legs drained of strength. A single question filled his mind; it was more important now than ever.

'Why did you prevent me from dying?' Tom's voice fell to a whisper, his words filled with emotion. 'In the car, on the ice and out there on the planet's surface – why did you keep me alive? Why am I still here?' Everything he had grappled to understand felt on the verge of falling apart.

The reply was sarcastic. Mr. Lampard's voice filled with deceit. 'You have no concept of what is to come.'

'What do you mean - what haven't you told me?

Mr. Lampard grinned. 'Something that will change everything.'

CHAPTER 52

The dome faded and Tom found himself in the open, the Martian surface a shock after the semi-darkness of the enclosed space. He inhaled tentatively, aware of the implications of Mars' toxic atmosphere, but found the air breathable.

His skin felt instantly chilled by the low temperature, but the air was warmer than it had been for billions of years. With tons of water vapour dumped into the atmosphere by the bludgeoning impact of Phobos, and the planet's fall towards the sun, its thin protective shell had changed dramatically. Low clouds now billowed overhead, their increasing bulk a sign of precipitation, and Tom realised rainstorms were building for the first time in billions of years.

He stepped over a low ridge as gritty dust blew against his unprotected skin. It swirled, causing him to shiver, but his attention was instantly drawn by a line which cut across the surface of the rock. It curved gently, forming a narrow channel barely wide enough to allow his fingers entry, and he found its sides perfectly smooth. A second and third line ran parallel to it less than a metre away where they intersected three concentric circles.

'What are these?'

'They extend across the plateau,' said Mr. Lampard. 'They are part of a more complex design.'

Tom looked to his right and saw another set of channels. He moved to study them, and came across an inscription.

The markings were angular, their short strokes crossing back and forth like scratches around the edge of a much larger circle. He knelt and traced the markings, but as his fingertips touched their smooth surface, a shock flooded his body and he cried out. His mind exploded in pain as his consciousness suddenly absorbed vast quantities of information.

After a few moments the pain subsided, and Tom closed his eyes until his head had cleared. When he looked up he felt fresh, as though cleansed by the experience, and stepped lightly over to Mr. Lampard.

A long silence hung between them. Finally, Tom spoke. 'The markings - you don't understand them, do you? They were written by your own people, but you've lost the ability to read them.' He rocked back on his heels as realisation kicked in. '*That's* why you've been protecting me. *That's* why you've brought me here; you need to know what the markings say, and you believe I can read them.' He faced Mr. Lampard with renewed confidence, and the old man shuffled uncomfortably. Tom knew his words had struck a nerve, and encouraged, he carried on. 'The fact that I'm here tells me you have a problem; it tells me the thing you want - the thing you *desperately* need - ' he paused, savouring the moment, 'is me.'

A fresh wind caught Tom unprepared, and he rubbed at his eyes to push away the dust. *Why is he so desperate to understand the markings?* he thought. *What is it that's so important here?* He studied the old man's careworn face, now no more than a disguise; a façade to hide the truth, and pondered the scale of events. *What does he really want?*

Tom scratched the stubble on his chin, yet despite all the lies and deceit which surrounded him, he sensed something was very wrong. When he spoke, his voice was terse. 'Tell me what I should know. If you want me to help, then tell me everything.'

Mr. Lampard was flippant, his body language dismissive, but Tom pressed his advantage. 'If you want me to dig you out of whatever hole you're in, you're going to tell me what all this is for.' He indicated the rock patterns beneath his feet. 'It's something major, I'll grant you that, but if you want my help...'

Mr. Lampard's tone was cautious and calculating, and Tom knew he was attempting to cover his tracks. 'This planet offered something we had not found anywhere - the possibility of rebirth which would have prevented us from growing old. It would have prevented us from dying.'

'You mean you would have cheated death?'

Mr. Lampard's words flowed with ease as a confident air settled over him. 'We found that somehow life had evolved on this world naturally. It possessed a strength we could combine with our own, and by matching it with our own DNA we could have created a unique form of life. We would have had the opportunity to develop far beyond our current existence.'

He paused briefly. 'It would have given us so much,' he said. His eyes flared, his voice suddenly brittle. 'On this world, we would have become gods!'

CHAPTER 53

'You want to be gods?' Tom was unable to contain his laughter. It washed over him like a wave.

'You find something funny?' The old man moved closer, his face set in a ferocious scowl.

'Gods?' repeated Tom. 'Are you serious?' His mouth twitched and he felt laughter rise again, but did not attempt to conceal it. 'What do I find funny?' he said. 'Don't you know?' Mr. Lampard's presence was threatening, but Tom continued. 'You mean you can't see it – you can't see the farcical nature of the situation?'

Mr. Lampard exuded loathing, and Tom realised he was on the edge of the old man's anger becoming something more. He attempted to stifle his laughter, and after several attempts felt some degree of control return. He looked into the old man's eyes, and realised the man he thought he knew had vanished.

'You once told me there was life everywhere in the universe; that it was all based on human DNA – our DNA – ' he indicated them both, 'but no matter how many planets you seeded, the life you left behind always failed.' Tom's lips held back a smirk. 'You dream of being god-like, yet everything you touch dies.'

The old man spat his reply. 'In the past we failed, but now…'

Tom cut him off. 'Now, if you managed a rebirth - however small - what good would it do you? You would be gods in a failing universe.'

Mr. Lampard's grin faded. He stepped nose to nose with Tom and a cold spark of intent flashed through his eyes, his breath a faint perfume of something from long ago. His words were no more than a whisper, their tone a sneer. 'If only you knew the possibilities, you would not be so flippant.' Mr. Lampard snarled. 'There is so much your limited world has yet to see. You are nothing but children, lost in the vastness of the universe.'

Tom felt uncomfortable with Mr. Lampard's presence. He didn't trust him. The old man's tone was threatening, but he did not want to step back and give ground: it would be seen as a victory, and would be seized upon.

'So, why did you bring me here?'

The old man's gaze did not waver, but his words softened slightly. 'You can decipher the secrets left behind on this planet. That in itself is a great power - a power over birth and death, history and future.'

'But if this planet is dead, why do you want me to decipher these markings? What good will it do?' Tom indicated the scarred landscape with its carved patterns and symbols. 'You once told me the Elders had decided your race should fade away and die quietly, yet here you are telling me there is something important hidden on this world. What haven't you told me?'

Mr. Lampard's gaze remained unmoving as he considered how much he should reveal. Finally he pressed on. 'In the early days of this world it had been decided that a record of our existence should be made, and the marks before you were left by the Elders for that purpose. But when this world died all faith was lost in those who had led us here, and they were removed from power.'

Tom interrupted. 'But the asteroid was a natural disaster - even *you* couldn't have prevented that from happening.'

Mr. Lampard conceded failure. 'As we watched this planet die, we saw in your world the opportunity for a second chance. It was not dissimilar to the world we had first chosen, but there were those who did not believe its seeding would produce anything of worth. The decision to proceed caused unrest within the An'Tsari race.'

Tom considered the old man's words. 'But your experiment wasn't a complete failure - the fact that we have evolved sufficiently to achieve space flight is a sign of success. We could so easily have destroyed ourselves many times over – we came close on a number of occasions.'

'Yes, but a fragment of the asteroid which caused this world to die struck your world millions of years later. We feared it would repeat the same devastation it had wrought here, but your world was spared the worst. It was the not the largest impact Earth has suffered, but it wiped out much of the life we had seeded, and plunged your world into turmoil.'

Tom recalled the asteroid that had struck Earth's surface sixty-five million years ago. It had pounded a hole nearly two-hundred kilometres wide into Mexico's Yucatán Peninsula, shrouding the planet in a thick blanket of dust which caused temperatures to plunge, and was associated with the extinction of the dinosaurs. It seemed a common thread linked the fates of both worlds.

Mr. Lampard spoke slowly, his voice distant. 'When we saw the carnage left behind, many felt the final opportunity for survival had passed beyond our grasp, and chose to leave.'

'But *you* chose to stay.'

Mr. Lampard pursed his lips. 'A small group of An'Tsari believed it was possible that life would rise from the ashes of your world, and set about hiding a message in the hope that one day it would be found, and you would discover the truth.'

'Why not simply tell us?'

'We needed proof you could handle the information. Should you not be ready it could throw your beliefs, your whole existence into turmoil, and that could restrict your evolution. It could ultimately bring about your own destruction.' Mr. Lampard indicated the markings. 'The circles beneath your feet represent the history of the An'Tsari people. They are a record of our existence; everywhere we have been and everything we have done has been recorded within them, and by deciphering their meaning you would learn the truth behind your own evolution.'

Tom scuffed at the surface with his boots. 'And you think I can read these markings - you think I can help you out of your predicament?'

Mr. Lampard's tone cooled once more. 'Your brain is rapidly

developing beyond anything the human species has ever known. In time, others will follow as evolution spreads throughout the human race. But for now there is only you.'

Tom understood. 'And the message you left behind was embedded where it would be discovered. '

'Yes, but its precise meaning would only be detected by those who showed a highly advanced level of intelligence.'

Tom remembered the images he had seen aboard the An'Tsari vehicle. 'And you hid this message within crop circles, where it would be disregarded by all but those who were sufficiently advanced?'

The old man grunted. 'Many patterns were believed to be fake – indeed, there were those on your world who relished the creation of fake patterns, and for many years they were regarded as nothing more than forgeries - but amongst them were precise mathematical formulae which we hoped you would identify.'

'Did we?'

Mr. Lampard shrugged. 'There was one who saw the designs for what they were, but he fell short of grasping their message. He shared his findings with others in the hope of deciphering the truth, but he was ignored. Although his mind was evolving, his mental abilities were insufficient. He died without completing his work.'

'So you used MAJESTIC as a cover, as a way to infiltrate the governments of the world and watch as humans evolved,' said Tom. It wasn't a question. It was a definition of understanding.

'Yes, but when our existence was discovered it was decided there was a need to take a more active role in humanity's evolution. We believed we could do more if we were directly involved with your greatest minds, and the creation of MAJESTIC presented the perfect opportunity.'

'When was that?' Tom had seen the files but wanted to be sure. He wanted to hear the truth first hand.

'After an An'Tsari ship crashed, a meeting between human and An'Tsari representatives was arranged, and an agreement reached. Shortly afterwards, MAJESTIC was formed to allow us to work together with your scientists. Through that alliance we secretly hoped we could stimulate the development of human intelligence, and safeguard our own future.'

'Who knew about MAJESTIC?'

Mr. Lampard's eyes flashed a sparkle of deep secrets. 'Only a select number of individuals. For many years your governments believed they were running their own scientific programmes, but in reality they were being controlled by higher forces.'

'By you?'

Mr. Lampard considered his response carefully. 'Yes, but when it became difficult to maintain our secrecy from outsiders it was decided we should relocate here.' The old man looked across the barren landscape. 'Unfortunately, we underestimated your planet's thirst for knowledge. Humanity proved to be more resourceful than we had presumed, and even on this world our safety was not guaranteed.'

A familiar sensation tingled the inside of Tom's forehead, and an image revealed itself. 'A probe from your world transmitted a series of images before we were able to intercept them,' said Mr. Lampard. 'The potential for damage was vast.' Tom had seen the images before: a perfectly straight line, white against the inky blackness of space, and deep within the shadow of Phobos. It had cast an elliptical shadow across the surface of the planet below, capturing a network of intricate lines on the surface.

'Phobos 2. It was a Russian probe,' said Tom. 'It revealed something we've never been able to explain,' he looked up at Mr. Lampard, 'but it found these markings, didn't it?' He indicated the lines where they stood. Tom knew he was right. Why else would the probe have suddenly stopped transmitting?

The image changed to a flower-shaped object, its highly reflective petals open to catch the weak rays of the distant sun.

'We were almost compromised on another occasion when a probe from your world landed in a sensitive location. The decision was made to shut its systems down before it could reveal anything of importance.'

Tom recognised Beagle 2. He remembered the

disappointment he had felt at its failure, but it was not until Mars Imager had returned photographs in 2016 that scientists realised the probe had reached the planet as intended. Now, Tom understood why it been unable to transmit its data home.

The images faded. 'So you remained hidden, but did you succeed in enhancing human intelligence?'

Mr. Lampard's expression was thoughtful. 'There was one who showed advanced mental capabilities...' He looked hard at Tom, and Tom knew instantly. Somehow he had always known.

'You have an ability to do great things,' said Mr. Lampard. He stepped closer and his voice shrank to a terse whisper. 'It is a power you do not yet understand, and it comes with great responsibility.' He paused and his eyes burned into Tom's. 'If your species is to evolve, you must learn how to use it.'

CHAPTER 54

Tom found himself back within the great dome, but this time it was different. The atmosphere swirled slightly, its air currents disturbing the light which pierced the room from above like a veil of mist. It shimmered with a hypnotic kaleidoscope of blues and purples, like oil on water.

Where the interior space had once been empty, a structure now rose from the ground far below. Four gantries extended outwards at right angles from it towards the walls of the chamber, yet despite the addition of the structure the chamber appeared larger than it had previously.

'This is the Gateway,' said Mr. Lampard. Pride gushed as he surveyed the open space. 'It is a passageway to all that we have been. It is a pathway to the past.' He turned away and busied himself with some task before facing Tom once more. 'Are you ready?'

'For what?' Tom felt uneasy. He had been thrust into something he did not fully understand, and wanted to know more before he made any decisions. He decided to play the situation cautiously.

'For what you have always been destined to do.' Mr. Lampard's voice rose in anticipation.

Tom shook his head in a gesture of innocence. 'You told me that once before, a long time ago.'

When Mr. Lampard had visited Tom's child mind, he had been too young to understand. It was only now, as he stood before the Gateway, that he began to grasp the immensity of his own position.

Mr. Lampard spread his arms wide as he continued, his words echoing in the vastness. 'This will assure you can accomplish your task.'

There was nothing before him but an empty room, and Tom snorted in disbelief. 'My task?'

'The secrets of this place go beyond anything your world could ever comprehended - until now.' He strode along the gantry, his feet echoing on the metalwork. 'The circles you found on your world...'

'The crop circles?'

Mr. Lampard continued without pause, '...were created to draw you here. They contained mathematical, astronomical and temporal data which, when decrypted, would prove to be elements of a map indicating the origins of all life.'

Tom feigned ignorance. 'Temporal data, what's that?'

'Oh, come now, do not play games with me.' The old man cast a withering stare, his gaze cold and calculating. 'This Gateway will provide access to everything that has gone before: our experiences in a thousand universes, and our seeding of a million worlds.' His eyes shone as he spoke, his face filled with an expression of gleeful delight. 'It will open the past as simply as turning the pages of a book.'

'And you expect me...'

'...to open the Gateway.' Mr. Lampard's words filled the empty space between them. 'Finally, after thousands of years of waiting, you are the one who can open the Gateway and take us back.' Mr. Lampard pulled himself up to his full height as the great domed surface shimmered into life above him. Patterns unfolded and sweeping arcs of light assembled themselves from a billion sparks into a swirl of stardust. He smiled.

A sudden pulse of blue-white light burst from somewhere below the gantry, followed instantly by a crackle of sound. It echoed from the walls of the chamber as it burst upwards, the icicle-like spires high above absorbing the sudden energy to glow with a luminous after-fire. The haze danced like dust particles caught in the early morning sun, billowing outwards to fill the dome with a million tiny points of light. They fanned outwards, forming galaxies and nebulae in miniature detail so perfect, Tom believed he could have been peering through a window into the universe.

As the dome filled, Tom found himself within a three dimensional model of a galaxy. Its planets and stars revolved slowly against the blackness, and he was stunned by the beauty of the moment. He reached out a tentative finger to touch the swirling mist, but the pinpoints passed over his fingers like a delicate rain of trickling sand, and carried on unhindered. His senses reeled at the complexity of the vision.

Uplifted by the moment, he felt free. Soaring amongst the stars, a warm and familiar presence washed over him. Its spiritual quality caused him to reach out for something – someone – as though he could touch their presence, but the sensation vanished as swiftly as it had arrived, and for a moment he felt sadness.

The old man stood immersed in the vision, his head back and arms raised as a cocoon of light enveloped him. His form faded to a ghostly silhouette, its details erased by the shimmering radiance, but finally the haze began to settle and a figure he had not seen in over thirty years stood before him. It was the same figure that had once immersed his sister in tendrils of purple-white light, and was a vision he had hoped never to witness again.

As he watched, the figure split into two distinct bodies. Standing slightly shorter, the second figure continued to take on detail as it composed itself from the dancing particles. It remained tantalisingly devoid of features as it twisted and billowed in the photons of light, its hair streaming as though caught in a flurry of summer wind. Finally, the light dimmed and the figure took a tentative step forward.

A vision of beauty smiled back at Tom, and his breath caught suddenly in his throat. The figure swept a wisp of hair from its face and angled its head slightly, the expression familiar, the smile as warm and inviting as he remembered. And at that moment Tom Richards felt his entire world finally come apart.

It was Annie.

CHAPTER 55

Tom choked, his throat tight with the intensity of emotion as Annie smiled. Her image was just as he remembered; her hair cascading in thick waves over her shoulders, and her eyes dark and intense against her pale skin. A thin scattering of freckles accentuated her delicate features, and Tom felt his mouth parch. He knew, without question, that he had missed her more than he had ever realised.

The surrounding light dimmed to a haze and Annie raised her arms. Her smile captivated him.

Tom remembered his final glimpse as she had closed the door between them all those years ago. He had relived it every day since, and saw it again now as she smiled. The scent of her perfume had haunted his memories throughout the years, and he had never given up hope that one day he would find her waiting for him. Now, as she stood before him, he found himself unable to speak.

Could this really be her?

Could this really be his Annie?

The world had moved on - twenty years had passed - yet here she was, no older than the twenty-one years of her youth; the age she had been when she had vanished.

Tom wanted desperately to believe that the young woman before him was the Annie Hope he had loved, but logic told him she couldn't be real; she couldn't be here. Not now. It was impossible.

He looked to the glowing figure behind Annie, and his voice cracked as he spoke. 'Why are you doing this? Why Annie?' His question was filled with twenty years' suppressed emotion. It echoed like a whisper of the past.

But when Annie spoke her voice was soft and smooth, and

Tom felt something inside him tug. 'It's me, Tom. It really is.' She smiled, and Tom felt himself as captivated as he had always been.

But it's not Annie. She's not really here. He shook his head as she stepped forward, a voice of reason calling him back to reality. 'No. No. You can't be.' His voice cracked under the emotion and hot tears stung his eyes. They rolled across his dust-streaked face unnoticed.

Annie reached up and tenderly wiped the tears away with her thumb. She tilted her head slightly to one side and smiled. 'I'm so glad you're here. I'm so pleased to see you.' She wrapped her arms around his neck and at first Tom resisted, mumbled rejections of her existence tumbling from his lips, but somehow, despite the logic of the moment, he knew it was her.

Long moments passed as they held each other, until Annie finally pulled away. She held Tom by his elbows and smiled up into his face. 'There's something you have to know. It's going to be hard for you to hear, but it's the truth.' She gazed into his eyes, tugged gently at his elbows until he focused on her, and then continued. 'Tom, are you listening?' She took hold of his right hand and squeezed. The gesture was returned, and he nodded.

Tom let out a deep breath and pinched his eyes closed to stem the tears that had formed there. 'Yes,' he whispered at last. 'Yes, I'm listening.'

Annie smiled. She spoke tenderly, but her voice betrayed the pain she felt at having to destroy Tom's memories of their past. 'I'm sorry, but I was never able to share something with you; I was never able to share the truth of who I really was.' She paused for a moment, as though preparing herself for the words she had never been able to speak, and then continued softly. 'Tom, I'm sorry, but I was always different and could never have been who you wanted me to be.' Her voice was clear and soft, her words the ultimate comfort to his ears after all he had suffered. 'I was always An'Tsari.'

Tom recoiled. 'No! Not after all we went through together,

after all we shared - it can't be true! I don't believe you!' He broke the contact between them and stepped back.

'Tom, it's the truth. It always was.'

'But why didn't you tell me?'

'I couldn't.' Pain filled her voice and it dropped to a whisper. 'I wasn't allowed to.' She reached out and took his fingers lightly. 'You simply weren't ready.'

Tom wiped at his eyes. 'Where did you go? Why did you leave?'

Annie dropped her gaze, her voice guilt-ridden. 'I had to.'

'Why? Weren't we good together?'

Annie's expression pulled at Tom's heart. 'That was the problem: we were *too* good, but we were worlds apart.' She paused and her voice sank again. 'Literally worlds apart.'

Annie let the words sink in and chose her moment carefully before continuing. 'Tom, I was sent to watch over you. I was sent to keep you safe. We were never meant to become involved as we did.' Annie smiled. 'Obviously our genes are not all that different, even after billions of years of evolution.'

Tom's voice was thick, the words filled with lost memories. 'But you loved me.'

'I know.' Her words were full of affection, her gaze that of the loving woman he had known so long ago. 'And that was why I had to leave.'

Tom side-stepped Annie and glared angrily at the glowing figure who had pretended to be Mr. Lampard. He raised his voice in anger. 'Who else did you plant in my life? Who else did you trick me with?' he shouted. 'Who else was there?'

The light became brighter as though in reaction, and Tom shouted again. 'My mother? My father? Who else was there in my life who wasn't the person I thought they were?' Neither Annie nor the glowing form answered. 'Who else?' Tom bellowed. His voice echoed around the open space.

Tom remembered the vision he had witnessed in the library; it had changed his life forever, and the glowing form before him resurrected the terrifying memory with a jolt. He had tried so hard to bury it over the years, but now, with a cold jolt of fear, he remembered every minor detail.

Abi! Oh,no! Please God, no! He grasped Annie by the shoulders. 'Please tell me Abi wasn't part of this.'

Annie placed her hands gently on Tom's forearms and spoke slowly, her words calming. 'Not in the way you think.'

'Not in the way that I think? What the hell's that supposed to mean?' Tom had rarely raised his voice to Annie, but it cracked now as he did so.

'Abi was not An'Tsari, but we used her as a Watcher. We saw through her eyes and heard through her ears. She aided us in observing what happened to you.'

'You used my sister to spy on me?' It all made sense now. He turned his back on Annie as his emotions bubbled. He couldn't bear to look at her.

'It was necessary to protect you. She didn't know - I promise you - but we were able to use her as a way of keeping you alive.'

'So you could bring me here.' Tom spoke coldly, every word a bitter taste in his mouth as he spat them.

Annie reached for Tom again and he felt her warm hands on his neck. 'Tom, please don't be angry. Know this: we did it to protect our existence - *all* our existences.' She indicated all three of them as she spoke. 'Every past has something worth saving.' The words hung in the air before she added, 'and I need you to do something for me.'

Annie glanced towards the glowing figure and a brief expression of concern passed over her face. When she turned back she was composed once again. 'For us.'

Tom's eyes remained tightly closed, his breathing erratic as Annie gently touched him again. 'Tom, do you hear me? We need you to do something.' She waited for him to respond, but he remained silent. His body was tense, his skin sensitive to the lightest touch of her fingers. When at last he opened his eyes she was smiling. 'Tom, it's important.'

Blood thudded in his ears as he considered everything that had happened. *What have I got to lose?* he thought. *What more can happen to destroy my life?* He looked at Annie and felt a rush of emotion as he studied her dark eyes and freckled nose. For a moment he was back in the years they had shared together, and knew that he would do anything for her.

Finally, with a squeeze of Annie's hands, he nodded. 'Okay. What do you want me to do?'

'There is somewhere we need to go.'

Tom could barely speak. 'Where?'

Annie took Tom's face between her palms and kissed him.

'It's not where, Tom, it's when.'

CHAPTER 56

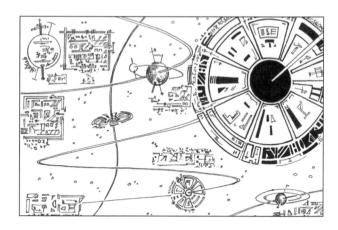

'Why didn't you tell me this in the first place? Why did you feel the need to be so secretive?'

Annie brushed her fingertips lightly across Tom's face. 'It was knowledge we could not allow you to possess, should you have failed in your own development.'

Tom closed his eyes as he struggled to understand everything he had heard. It made sense in a strange way, as though he had always known.

'Come.' Annie took him by the hand. They approached the centre of the sphere and a disc-shaped platform, topped by a circular control panel, shimmered into existence. Annie stepped through a narrow gap in the console and Tom followed. Without pause she touched an illuminated symbol, and panels around the console's smooth surface lit up. Their linear patterns, similar to the symbols he had found on the Martian surface, glowed in the darkness while their golden tracery illuminated Annie's face with soft light. Tom felt his breath taken away once again by her beauty.

'Everything has been assembled.' Annie indicated the glowing map of stars and galaxies above; a series of lines looped back and forth, and they stretched from planet to planet and sun to sun, shooting off suddenly in new directions.

Annie pointed. 'The links you see follow our route through space and time. They are a record of everywhere the An'Tsari have travelled - every parallel universe and every planet we have ever seeded.' She touched a control and the view changed. 'We can move in any direction through the life of this universe, and any number of others, our journey limited only by the routes we have travelled.'

Every universe was represented by a symbol, and as Annie touched one it quickly reorganised itself to show the galaxies contained within it. Lines and symbols criss-crossed their way through, looping around each other like cords, before passing through a series of spinning discs to vanish as though they had never existed.

Tom touched a symbol, and its swirling mass of light condensed. Galaxies rushed towards each other and merged into a giant super-galaxy. He stepped back as the vision solidified and rotated above him.

'Some galaxies do not break up,' said Annie. 'This galaxy was so vast it collapsed in on itself after a few billion years. Because of its great size it was so much hotter, its cycle of birth and death so rapid, that its planets only existed for a few million years before they were consumed.'

Tom manipulated the controls before him, his movements instinctive as though he had worked them countless times. A column flickered into existence behind him, and it filled the centre of the workstation like the axle of the great wheel. Strange yet familiar symbols were arranged across its surface in a pattern of concentric circles, and a large icon Tom recognised from the Martian surface was set at the centre of each group.

'These are the instructions for the Gateway.' Annie indicated the ring shaped console around the edge of the platform. 'They are familiar to us. With them we have been able to plot our route through the past, but these controls,' she indicated the complex array of symbols on the central axis, 'are unfamiliar. We cannot manipulate them.'

Tom inhaled deeply and held his breath for a moment as he studied the symbols. Finally, he looked at Annie. 'And you believe I can.'

She smiled. Tom felt himself drawn, yet something held him back. He peered intently at Mr. Lampard. *He's lied to me all this time*, he thought, *but surely Annie wouldn't do the same - not after everything we once were?* Tom had trusted Annie implicitly. But now? She smiled and he felt himself tugged between reality and the desire to have her in his life again. *But she isn't human; she isn't the woman I always thought she was*. He looked into her dark eyes and saw there was something else, something held back.

'What haven't you told me?'

Annie looked uneasy. She shuffled, her words jumbled before she was able to gather her thoughts. When she spoke again her words were carefully chosen. 'We tried to open the Gateway ourselves, but failed.' She sighed. 'We had to rely on a certain amount of guesswork, but it was not enough.' She looked away, embarrassed at admitting failure. 'The Gateway is usually opened in the heart of a dying star, and we convert its energy into a form we can use.' She paused as though unsure of how to continue, but picked up her explanation without faltering. 'We placed a converter into the heart of your star when we first arrived here, so we could control its energies.'

Tom raised his eyebrows. 'And what - exactly - does this converter do?'

Annie considered. 'Simply, it takes the core's raw energy and focuses it into a unique pattern. Without it, the Gateway cannot be opened.'

Tom realised with a cold jolt what the An'Tsari had attempted. 'In the absence of a dying star you thought...' He couldn't believe what he had just heard. 'You used the raw energy of a *living* star instead!'

Annie nodded slowly.

'*Our* star!' He was disgusted. He turned away and rubbed his hands through his hair, frustration and disbelief evident in every movement. When he faced Annie once more his voice was hard. '*That* was what caused the solar flare and the storm; *that* was what caused the planet to slip out of orbit and Phobos to fall!' It was irresponsible and the truth horrified him. 'How could you do that? You *must* have known the danger you were creating!' Tom directed his anger at Mr. Lampard. 'You caused an irreversible change in the balance of the solar system, which in time will affect the orbit of everything orbiting the sun – every planet, moon and asteroid. Everything!' He walked away in disgust and gripped the edge of the console. 'What would have happened if you'd succeeded? Did you even *consider* the damage you could have inflicted?'

Annie attempted to calm the situation. She approached Tom slowly and placed her hand on his arm. It had always a calming gesture, but did not work this time. He threw off her touch but she replaced it. She spoke calmly. 'Tom, opening the Gateway creates a rip in the fabric of space which your science understands as a wormhole. Once open, it can be used whenever the need arises, allowing us to travel through space and time without the need to find a dying star each time. We prefer to use a dying star, but with a healthy star the amount of energy taken creates only a minor dip in the star's output.' Annie shrugged. 'Opened properly the effect should have been insignificant, but something went wrong. The solar storm was an unexpected side effect.' She paused. 'I'm sorry.'

Mr. Lampard spoke for the first time since Annie had stepped out of the light. 'When the Elders were removed from power, they refused to co-operate with us.'

'And you were arrogant enough to think you could open the Gateway without their knowledge.' Tom had little patience left, his anger fuelled by the old man's presence, but Mr. Lampard continued unfazed. 'Within the ruling council of Elders there was one who could open a Gateway, but during the change of power he was involved in an...accident.' Tom detected the hesitation in Mr. Lampard's words, but he was too furious to question it. The old man continued. 'The Gate Master died during the struggle. Consequently, we were left with incomplete information.'

'You mean you couldn't read the symbols,' finished Tom. 'You tried anyway, just in case you hit on the right combination, but you couldn't do it and had to concede defeat.' Tom forced himself to remain calm; he knew he needed to stay in control, despite everything he had learned. 'So, you needed someone who could interpret for you, and you thought I would do.' He felt enraged, but at last understood why the An'Tsari had persevered in their attempt to enhance the human race. He fixed Annie and Mr. Lampard with a stare, his lips pursed into a thin line. 'Now I know why you said I was The One. At the end it all comes down to me.' He raised his arms and dropped them against his sides in exasperation. 'I suppose your little plan makes perfect sense.'

Annie spoke softly. 'With your evolved mental capabilities, we believe you will be able to open the Gateway. If you cannot, then the last remnants of the original An'Tsari race will die here. We are the last, Tom. We need you.'

'And what happens if I can *safely* open it?'

'If you can, then we can return to the First Days and provide ourselves with DNA samples which will prevent our own deaths.'

'So, basically, you will tell your own people what is going to happen in the future, in the hope they can prevent it from ever happening. You're going to overwrite the defective gene like overwriting a computer file with a more up-to-date program.' He fell silent as something else struck him. 'You're intending to use the evolved human DNA to overwrite the defects in your own genetic code, but without me, you have nothing.' He smiled at the simplicity of it all. 'You need my DNA, you need my intellect, and you need my co-operation to open the Gateway. In short, you need me.'

'Yes. If you look at it that way, I suppose you're right.' Mr.

Lampard appeared smug, but as Tom looked away he recognised something in Annie's face from all those years ago - a nervous shift in her eyes, a flicker that he read instantly, and he knew that something was amiss.

CHAPTER 57

'What happens when we've passed through the Gateway? Will the planets be affected by our passage?'

'A controlled jump should only take enough energy from your sun to open the Gateway,' replied Annie. 'It should not create another solar storm.'

'Should not, or will not? That doesn't exactly fill me with confidence.' Tom's expression showed his lack of confidence in the process. 'I don't like being so vague about the safety of my home world.'

Mr. Lampard stood side by side with Annie. 'There can never be total certainty about the effects of the Gateway, but all previous evidence indicates the point of departure remaining unaffected.'

'Great. Now you tell me it's not even guaranteed that passage through this thing is safe,' huffed Tom. 'My day just keeps on getting better.' He walked once around the outer console before returning to face Mr. Lampard. 'And then there's the issue of what happens when you've done whatever it is you're planning to do: can we return here, or do we stay in your universe? As nice as I'm sure your universe is, I want to return home, whether we make it back to Earth or not. This is where I belong, and I want to be with my friends – whether of not they are still alive.'

'The other members of your crew are safe; that I can guarantee.' Mr. Lampard stepped through a gap in the outer console and strode off along a gantry. He paused long enough to open a hatch in the wall of the sphere. 'You can visit them if you wish.'

Tom acknowledged the offer. 'Now?'

Mr. Lampard paused within the opening. 'Come.'

Is this another trick? Tom thrust his fists into his pockets and chewed at his bottom lip as he mulled over the offer. *But what's the worst that can happen?* he thought. *After all, I have the upper hand. If he's lying again I can always refuse to open the Gateway.* He grunted in indecision, but stepped towards the hatch and bobbed through. Mr. Lampard stood waiting as Tom slid inside. The hatch closed behind them and began its cycle. *Airlock*, he thought. *We must be in an exposed area.*

Mr. Lampard's attack caught Tom by surprise. He found himself thrust suddenly against the bulkhead, and his head bounced against the cold metal. His vision disintegrated into a red mist as blood streamed from a gash above his eyes. Sickening pain blurred his sight and he tried to turn, but Mr. Lampard's grip was too powerful.

Tom felt his cheek pressed hard against the bulkhead and a voice whispered harshly into his ear, its breath hot on the side of his face. 'We're going outside for a little talk where we will be...undisturbed.' The final word came out in a slow drawl, and Mr. Lampard gave a shallow laugh. 'I suggest you think carefully about your decision to open the Gateway: refusal is not an option.'

Tom was gripped hard, the fingers buried deep in his neck as the outer hatch slid open. He was thrown forward onto the Martian surface and turned quickly, ready to face his attacker, but the figure which stepped from the airlock was not human. Its eyes startled Tom the most, their almond shape distorting the world with their cold intent. They chilled him.

Tom recalled the babbling Danny Forbes as he lay terrified and distraught on their sofa over thirty years ago. The visitor had been terrified by the dark eyes of the An'Tsari, his sleep disturbed by memories of abduction and examination, and Tom understood now just how frightened Danny had been. But on Mars, things were different. Here, knowledge was power: Tom could refuse to open the Gateway if he chose, and it was an option he had every intention of carrying out if he was not convinced the An'Tsari plan was safe.

Tom blinked his eyes to clear them as the wind whipped sand

into his face. He squinted against the squall to protect his sight, and saw the figure transform itself further as it approached. It hissed in his ear, and Tom whipped around. 'You're nothing more than a stepping stone towards the true potential of the An'Tsari.' The figure spat in disgust. 'Your whole race is nothing but a pale imitation. Even in the first days of our evolution, you could never have matched us. We were superior even then, and we will be again.'

It leant closer, its body menacing. 'Now, if you do *exactly* as I tell you, your co-operation will guarantee the survival of your friends.' Tom felt fingers on the back of his neck again, the grip hard as it bit into his flesh. He twisted in an attempt to break the hold, but the grip intensified. The voice hissed into his ear. 'And your sister.'

Tom gagged as the words struck home. His anger boiled and he struggled to escape, but felt himself thrown. He struck the ground with his shoulder, pain lancing through it as he scraped across bare rock, and rolled to his knees. He cradled his injured shoulder in an effort to protect it from the blow that he knew must follow, but it did not materialise.

Another figure stepped between them, and for an instant Tom saw double. The figures grappled as one, their bodies blurred between natural and chosen forms, and Tom saw many faces he recognised.

Annie forced Mr. Lampard down, grabbed him by the throat, and slammed his An'Tsari form against the airlock. He thrashed around as she held him in place, his arms and legs beating against her alien body as Tom dragged himself to his feet. Strange voices filled his head, their words of conflict a clash of sounds which jarred as though laid one on top of another, and within it, two words caught his attention:

Trust me.

The words were strong and meaningful, their presence calming.

I have convinced him that you will do as he asks, and will ensure your friends are safe, but you must co-operate by opening the Gateway. You must trust me.

Tom felt the connection about to break, but in the dying seconds he sent a question. *What about Abi? If he hurts her...*

Trust me.

As he felt Annie's words again, he realised he had no room for manoeuvre. If he wanted everyone to remain safe, there was nothing else he could do.

CHAPTER 58

The console hummed as Tom studied its symbols, each representing a numerical value as well as one of the fifty-two letters of the An'Tsari alphabet. In combination they were part of a larger numerical grid, and had to be activated in the correct sequence, otherwise the huge generators beneath the dome would not draw safely on the power of the sun. The result could be catastrophic.

The last time the sequence had been attempted the imbalance had caused a colossal solar flare. Had the error been greater, the resulting eruption could have destroyed all life on Earth. It was a mistake Tom was not willing to repeat.

Indicators flashed beneath his fingers as he entered the first sequence, and the arrangement of symbols changed as phase one ran its cycle. When all was complete the symbols flashed green, and he moved to the central axis of the control room. His fingers moved confidently over its surface, dragging groups of glowing indicators together and placing them in small pockets within a central panel. As each level completed its sequence the symbols changed colour, and finally satisfied he had calculated correctly, he dropped them into a central disc.

Over two hundred million kilometres away the converter buried within the sun's core came online, and power began to flow through its ancient systems. Once open, the Gateway would send them on a journey through the maze of wormholes the An'Tsari had created, and would project them back towards the home world. It was much like threading a needle through holes punctured in fabric, dragging a thread behind them to show their passage.

The same threads would later allow Tom to return to his own universe - or so he hoped.

CHAPTER 59

Annie stepped between the two men as the Gateway began its final cycle. She reached out towards Tom, but another presence joined her thoughts. Its entrance was sudden and Tom backed mentally away from it, but Annie's warmth steadied his nerve. He glanced up and saw the old man chuckle, his head dipped slightly as though attempting to hide his laughter.

'What is it? What's funny?' Tom's words were lost in the enormity of the room, but Mr. Lampard's eyes sparkled with a devious glint, and within that single moment, Tom realised everything he had been told was an elaborate lie.

The old man chuckled, the sound deep and throaty as he raised his arms high above his head. The voice filled Tom's head and his blood turned cold.

'Come, my brothers! Our task awaits us!' He grinned again, his eyes full of intent, each word more powerful than the last. 'The Gateway is opening and we can at last return home. Come - we are free!'

Tom cast his thoughts to Annie. *Whom is he calling? What does he mean?'*

I do not know. Annie shook her head. *He has not revealed any of this to me.* She pushed her consciousness towards the old man, but felt herself rebuffed. She recoiled under the pressure and Tom caught her as she fell. She placed her head in her hands as she struggled to clear her mind.

What happened? What did you see?

Nothing - he would not allow me entry. She placed a hand on Tom's shoulder. *I will try once more, but do not hold much hope of success.* Tom sensed worry in her thoughts. *I fear he has misled us both.*

The old man had turned his back on Tom and Annie, ignorant

of their presence as he thrust his arms to the sky. A circle of light cast itself down from above and a figure appeared briefly within it, but Tom recognised instantly that it was not human. It settled before Mr. Lampard and another took its place above. Behind it other lights formed, each with a shadow at their centre, and as the old man called out the Gateway suddenly picked up speed. The circle of light enclosed them, and darkness descended.

The central icicle high above suddenly came to life. It cast a brief pulse of light and a deep tone which was followed by others in succession. Each sound was discordant, but finally, like a great orchestra tuning up, their rhythms drew together into a single harmonious pulse, and the air vibrated with energy.

Annie steadied herself, her attempt to enter Mr. Lampard's mind something that would have to wait. She touched the palm of Tom's hand with her fingertips and they interlaced fingers as a final shadow appeared.

'Are we ready, my brothers?' Mr. Lampard spoke in a loud voice. The shadows above responded, their words confirmation of something long planned, some secret long hidden.

'Good, then let us begin.' The old man dropped his hands and turned at last towards Tom and Annie. He smiled as though seeing them for the first time, and snarled with contempt. 'And now, at last, we can accomplish everything of which we have dreamt. We can conclude matters as they should have been conducted a long time ago.'

'Who are they?' Annie indicated the lights and shadows. 'What have you done?' The old man did not reply, and as he turned away she lunged at him. She hoped to distract him long enough to allow entry to his mind, but he shrugged her away like an unwanted child. Tom grabbed Mr. Lampard by his collar and dragged him around. Like Annie, he too was thrown, and he fell against the curtain of light.

Tom rolled to his knees and froze, stunned beyond words by the arc of Mars as it lay before him like a great orange marble against the heavens.

The old man suddenly appeared by his side, his face

illuminated by the curtain of light. His snarl was accompanied by manic laughter as he twisted to take in the view, and he bellowed triumphantly in Tom's face. Spittle flew as he jabbered and ranted, and he threw an arm suddenly around Tom's shoulders. Tom tried to pull away, but the old man's grip was strong and he felt himself shaken. Mr. Lampard rocked back and forth excitedly, Tom dragged along with him.

A spark of reflected light caught Tom's attention against the distant horizon, and he stared intently as it grew in size. Others appeared in formation behind it, and a vast fleet of ships drifted into view as he watched. Their triangular hulls were familiar, their forms dark and brooding as they hovered above the surface of the planet, but something about them was different. Each ship bristled with spikes and pods, and Tom knew their intention was not peaceful. They slid beneath him, and Tom realised they were grouping to follow them through the Gateway.

'Isn't that a beautiful sight?' shouted Mr. Lampard. He laughed again, and spittle sprayed across Tom's cheek for the second time, but he could only watch as the ships passed beneath him. They disappeared from view and he felt the breath squeezed from his lungs as their purpose struck home.

'Take a good look!' shouted Mr. Lampard. 'Take a good look at what you've done!'

CHAPTER 60

Mr. Lampard dragged Tom back into the chamber. He dropped him in a heap and Annie immediately went to him.

Why are you doing this? Her thoughts struggled to find entry to Mr. Lampard's consciousness, but found a crack in his guard and worked their way in. *Why?* she repeated. *It was never meant to be this way!*

How little you know, he responded, *but you need not concern yourself with such matters. Now, leave me!* The voice echoed and she felt dizzy under its power, and then the link was broken.

The wall of light surrounding the chamber began to dissolve. It fizzed and sparkled to reveal the space the sphere had once occupied, and Mars and its fleet of waiting ships drifted from view. Tom was transfixed as Earth passed overhead. He stared longingly as its crystal white ice caps, clear blue oceans and brown-green landmasses drifted past. He suddenly felt a deep longing to visit Earth one final time, and his eyes misted over as its beauty slipped away. He craned his neck to follow, but it was soon lost against the glare of the burning sun, and he felt a deep sadness unlike anything he had ever experienced.

The diamond-bright stars were gradually obliterated by the glare of the sun as it filled the heavens. Its light increased until it became almost unbearable, and as the Gateway directed them towards it Tom shielded his eyes. He pressed his palms hard against his face, but still the light intensified. It passed through flesh, then through bone, and he cried out in pain as his eyes were speared with points of searing light. Annie placed her arm around his shoulders and pulled him to her chest, but he was unaware of her touch as pain burnt through every nerve in his body.

With a sudden rush the sun rose to meet them, and they were thrust into its burning heart. Tom felt himself enveloped by its intense heat, his skin scorched by its touch... and then it was gone.

As the light dimmed, Tom slumped into Annie's arms. The Gateway had opened, and everything Tom Richards had ever known had vanished.

CHAPTER 61

Time raced backwards as universes existed in reverse. They appeared briefly and it became impossible to separate one from another, but finally their journey slowed and they entered an immense spiral galaxy. It resembled so many others, each planet like every other they had witnessed, until a single world revolved before them. Its surface was patched green and purple, and its cities shimmered with light and energy as they rose high above its surface. Its beauty was unmistakeable.

Swooping low between great buildings they saw smooth curves and arcs of crystal, familiar markings etched into their surfaces like brush strokes on an artist's canvas. Their design reflected the An'Tsari symbols Tom had encountered on the Martian surface, and the buildings were reminiscent of the natural structures he had encountered in his visions.

Road-like formations curled between the buildings while fields of green and purple lay spread far below. Spires and pinnacles ascended like the skyscrapers of Earth, and Tom was reminded of the open spaces from back home; places where people could walk and relax amid the bustle of city life. *We're not so different after all*, he thought. *Somehow, civilisation looks the same wherever we go.*

They passed over city after city, the An'Tsari homeworld composed of beautiful buildings unlike anything constructed on Earth, and then they raced quickly towards a vast ocean of violet and blue.

They dropped to skim the wave tops as twin suns glared unceasingly. For the second time, Tom felt the heat of the An'Tsari homeworld, and for a moment it warmed the chill which had crept into his body.

A smudge darkened the horizon, and Tom was reminded of

thunderclouds. Their twisted forms were angry and contorted, their colour tainting the sky with a darkness that Tom found unpleasant, and a wave of unease swept over him.

They dropped suddenly between towering columns of smoke into the burnt-out ruins of a city. Its beautiful buildings lay shattered and twisted by the great ships which hung menacingly in the sky, their energy beams lancing down to rip the surface of the planet apart. The ships left death and destruction in their wake, and Tom slumped to his knees as he watched them work their way across the broken city.

An explosion detonated directly in their path, and the curved form of a magnificent building twisted itself before his eyes. The skin of the building appeared to hang in the sky like a billion fragments of glitter as the explosion lifted them clear; and then, with a deafening report, the fragments vanished. Nothing remained of the magnificent building but a mangled skeleton of metal and fire. It curled upon itself like a dying animal, and Tom gripped the edge of the console for support. He couldn't believe the destruction he was witnessing.

Against the devastation, Tom heard a voice shout in triumph. Mr. Lampard's elation filled the silence between explosions with howls of excitement and laughter. Annie screamed as an explosion appeared directly in their path, and she cowered against Tom, but the blast passed over them with no effect. Further explosions rumbled and Tom shouted above the deafening sounds of war.

'Where are we? What is all this?' He struggled against the deafening sounds of destruction. 'What have you brought us to?'

Mr. Lampard's eyes blazed with the ecstasy of the moment. 'Where have I brought you? Don't you know?' He raised his clenched fists and shook them in defiance. 'War!' he shouted, his tone filled with exhilaration. 'This is the war that should have been! It's the last days of the battle for the An'Tsari homeworld!'

'Why? What do you hope to achieve?' If nothing else, Tom wanted to understand why he had been deceived.

'Why? Because it's exhilarating!' Mr. Lampard growled. He

cast Tom the smile of a mad man. His voice dropped to a husky whisper, his words full of menace. 'It is the war we should have won.'

Tom gasped for breath 'This is about winning a war you've already *lost?*'

Mr. Lampard snarled in triumph. 'And now, it's a war that can be won!'

'But how does returning here change anything? You'll just lose all over again.'

Mr. Lampard grinned. 'Not this time. Not after we right the wrongs of the past.'

'You mean you intend to change history?'

Annie climbed to her feet, her petite size putting her at a disadvantage, but she appeared unfazed by the old man's dominance. Her words were direct. 'You lied to me. You told me you could provide the means to live on, the means to live forever.'

Mr. Lampard laughed. 'And I will. I will end this war and plot a new course for the An'Tsari people. I will create a universe of conflict, a universe of domination, and I will begin with our own people. I will create a new breed of An'Tsari warriors. We will no longer be a race of peaceful wanderers, with no purpose but to harvest and seed. Look where that course took us - to our own death with nothing to show but a few markings on a dead world, and you with an affection for a weaker race.' He sniggered at Annie. 'By re-engineering the An'Tsari people, I will seed the worlds of every universe with life worth conquering. At last we will have a purpose worthy of our existence!'

'Building and destroying worlds, pitting An'Tsari against An'Tsari; is that really a future to be proud of? Is that all we've become?' said Annie. 'Have you learnt nothing from the people of his world?' Annie indicated Tom, but Mr. Lampard's stare did not falter.

The old man bent until his face was so close to Annie's that their noses were almost touching. 'What else is there? We have existed in peace for so long, searching for other worlds and the existence of life, yet have found nothing worthy of our time.' He turned away. 'The Elders were weak, but here, at the beginning, we were strong. Now *I* will take the strongest, *I* will take the most powerful of our people, and *I* will seed them across the universe. The new An'Tsari will have a future worth fighting for, and it will all be because of me!'

Annie spoke quietly, her voice filled with determination. 'I won't let you put this world onto a course which will destroy it,' she said, 'and I won't let you destroy every world you touch. That is not the way our people should exist.'

A huge explosion lit the sky with fire, and An'Tsa's twin suns appeared as glowing discs through the swirling smoke, all but obliterated by the pall of battle. Tom climbed to his feet and stood shoulder to shoulder with Annie.

'And what will you do?' Mr. Lampard's voice was filled with sarcasm, his question edged with a sneer.

'What will I do?' Mr. Lampard had told him that humans and An'Tsari were the same species, but if he let Mr. Lampard continue he would turn every part of history into a war of such terrible destruction that it may never recover. The truth of human-An'Tsari history would be lost forever in the shadows of the past, and that was something he could not allow to happen.

'What will I do?' he repeated. 'I will stand against you to protect my past and my future. Without history there is no future, and without freedom there is no space to evolve.'

Mr. Lampard closed the distance between them to a mere breath. When he spoke his voice was no more than a whisper, his face filled with a level of anger that Tom had not seen before. 'Your race does have spirit.' He smiled and pressed forwards. 'That is a good thing. It will make the conquering of your world all the sweeter.'

His eyes flashed as he took a final step forward. 'I hope you're ready,' he rasped, 'because I'm really going to enjoy this.'

CHAPTER 62

The old man's rage erupted with such fury that Tom was lifted from the floor and slammed against the console. He rolled to one side, but his left arm was pinned by the old man's weight. Tom wrestled to free himself, but his elbow and shoulder stabbed with pain as Mr. Lampard's weight bore down.

Fresh pain seared through Tom's shoulder as his feet slipped away, and his weight dropped towards the floor. He attempted to lever himself into a less painful position, but Mr. Lampard kept him pinned.

The old man's fist struck hard. Flowers of light and darkness streamed across Tom's vision and his eye socket exploded with pain. He recoiled, his head swimming, and struggled to clear some of the fuzziness that clouded his mind.

A dense fog remained, but from somewhere a familiar voice whispered. In his distraction Mr. Lampard's blow was crushing, and Tom crumpled under the old man's power. His feet slid away once more and he hung by his arm, the edge of the console digging painfully into his flesh. His boots scrabbled at the decking, catching and slipping away until one foot found a tentative grip, but the excruciating pain in his arm dragged at his consciousness, and he felt himself begin to slide. As the last of his strength ebbed, he drew his foot back and kicked out hard. The old man grunted and Tom realised he had struck a glancing blow, but the response was swift as he was struck across his shoulder. Fresh pain coursed through Tom's trapped arm and he knew he only had moments before it broke. If that happened he would have no way to defend himself from the onslaught, and any hope of stopping Mr. Lampard would be lost.

Remember son, the best form of defence is attack. Strike hard and strike fast.

Tom heard his father's words as though they were standing together. His father had always been a morally strong man and had never advocated violence, but now, at this moment, Tom believed his father would agree that Mr. Lampard had to be stopped.

Tom kicked out again and Mr. Lampard shifted position, allowing Tom to raise himself slightly. He placed his weight firmly on one foot and kicked upwards repeatedly with the other. The kick caught its intended target and Mr. Lampard howled with rage.

Tom dragged himself into an upright position and pressed his advantage. He jabbed high with his right boot and saw it strike Mr. Lampard's jaw. The old man lifted his weight further and Tom felt firm ground beneath him. Reaching out, he pushed hard, and the old man fell backwards onto the console. He had no time to react as Tom landed on top of him, his arms raised in a pitiful attempt at defence, and Tom pounded him with blow after blow. The old man writhed in protest, but finally the two bodies slipped to the deck and parted.

Tom hunched over as he sucked in huge lungfuls of air, but the figure before him rose with a confidence that caused him to despair. *How much more do I have to do?* he thought. *How much longer can this last?* His muscles felt weak with exertion, and his injured arm throbbed with pain.

Mr. Lampard sneered. 'An impressive start, I'll grant you, but is that all you have to give?' He made a sweeping gesture with his hands. 'More?'

Tom swallowed, but before he was ready Mr. Lampard rushed forward. He struck with ferocity, yet somehow Tom kept to his feet.

Dropping his body, Tom thrust himself into the attack and lifted the old man clear off the ground. He attempted to throw the body forward, but Mr. Lampard clawed and twisted, and Tom's grasp weakened. As the old man gathered his strength again Tom stepped quickly to one side, and forced his back into the charge.

Mr. Lampard was caught off guard and Tom seized the advantage. He stamped hard on an exposed foot and swept the old man's supporting leg from the ground as he dropped his weight to the right. His shoulder exploded in agony as the old man grappled for a hand-hold, but the pain was momentary as the figure slid over him towards the decking.

Without giving the old man time to recover, Tom dropped with his full weight. His knees crushed the body beneath him, pinning it to the floor, and he grasped the figure tightly by the throat. He ignored the frenzied clawing of hands and feet as his grip tightened, but could never have imagined the change that passed over Mr. Lampard as he lay beneath his hands.

Tom's grip weakened as the old man's face contorted into a terrifying image, but it was the eyes that affected him the most. They gleamed with evil intent, and Tom instinctively backed up. He saw his own fear reflected in their wide, unblinking appearance, and although he felt impelled to move, he found he could not. Tom knew he was finished.

Unable to prevent himself from being thrown, Tom landed on the cold decking. The old man crouched above, his rasping laugh hot in his face, and a single word floated through Tom's head. It filled every corner of his mind until he could hear nothing else.

Yield.

A female voice edged the word aside and a vision of Abi swam before his eyes. It encouraged him, and reminded him of his childhood. *Never give up! Never be beaten!*

Mr. Lampard angled his head as he sensed the presence. Tom knew the old man was looking within him, searching for something only Tom could see, and was forced to smile. The words gave him strength and he thrust his whole body upwards as his anger exploded. His back arched as if shocked by a bolt of electricity, and his knuckles smarted as his fist caught the old man across the chin.

'No! This is not going to happen! I won't let you!' Tom struggled to release himself, but fingers clawed at his windpipe and pain erupted inside his head. He forced his chin down in an effort to weaken the grip, but it was not enough, and the pressure on his throat intensified.

A rapidly narrowing tunnel formed as the edges of his vision began to close in. He sucked each painful breath through clenched teeth, his throat raw from the exertion and lack of oxygen, and as his eyes began to lose focus, the face before him changed. He recognised Harriman and Williams, as well as other faces he had known throughout his life. They swam before him, and Tom realised he had been surrounded on all sides for so many years by one man: Mr. Lampard.

A shadow passed between them, and the grip around his throat was suddenly released. Tom rolled over and gulped oxygen, his eyes closed as he struggled to control his ragged breathing. His chest was racked by deep coughs and he retched violently, but as he opened his eyes he saw Annie a short distance away. The figure of Mr. Lampard lay pinned beneath her, his arms and legs thrashing in an attempt to free himself. He hissed and snarled as Annie held him down, but she ignored him.

We must do something. He cannot be allowed to do this. Annie's words were filled with the emotion of deception. *We must stop him. We cannot allow this to happen – our ancestors were a peaceful race. You must believe me.*

Tom staggered to his feet, but Annie warned him to stay back. She turned back to the old man beneath her and forced her thoughts into his head, her power enough to quell some of his violence, but she found herself thrust aside and the old man scrambled to his feet.

In his weakened state Tom had no chance of deflecting the assault. Mr. Lampard gripped him savagely and hauled him above his head, but Tom hooked his arm around the old man's neck as his weight was thrown forward, and they tumbled together.

Tom cried out in pain as his injured arm crumpled beneath him, but Mr. Lampard was not so lucky. His head struck the edge of the console and he staggered, dazed by the impact, until his knees buckled and he slumped onto the deck.

It was the moment for which Tom had been waiting.

Annie took Tom's hand and they entered Mr. Lampard's mind together. Deep inside, they found mental fingerprints which Tom recognised. Their texture was familiar, their vibrations unpleasant, but he forced himself around them until he encountered something sharp. He hovered for a moment, composed himself, and then forced his way between its razor-like edges into the old man's subconscious mind.

At first he scouted its edges, as though testing the temperature of water before diving in, and watched the being he had always known as Mr. Lampard. The old man had visited Tom's sleeping mind on many occasions, and the experience had badly disturbed his sleep throughout childhood, but now Tom was inside that same mind. He recoiled as anger and aggression battered back and forth around him, and he forced himself to remain calm as it surrounded him. He couldn't allow it to find a weakness in his own mind; to do so would invite certain madness, and there was too much at stake for failure to be considered an option.

How has he managed to suppress this for so long? Tom shuddered. *With so much frustration, so much anger and hate, it's a wonder he hasn't destroyed himself.*

Tom moved away and felt the anger subside slightly, but the sensation of hate whirled once more, and he shrunk back. It battered against him in an effort to gain entry to his mind, and then vanished into the darkness. *It's as though he's unable to cope with others succeeding where he has failed*, thought Tom. *It's as though his mind has been twisted, and anger is his only outlet.*

Tom pressed on. He passed over many things he did not understand: visions of worlds, other humanoid beings he could only assume were the result of seeding in other universes, and was fascinated. Many of the beings he saw were much like him, although each had its own individuality. Part of him wanted to delve further, but time would not allow him to linger.

A face lunged from the darkness and Tom's heart hammered. He swallowed hard, the face aggressive, but it seemed unaware of his presence as he watched. He knew he must move on, but a scene began to play out before him and he stepped back, transfixed.

Soldiers moved from building to building, their weapons tearing the world apart before his eyes, and Tom realised he was seeing something of Mr. Lampard's vision. It mesmerised him and he had to pull back for breath, his body covered in a sheen of sweat, but Annie's mind suddenly wrapped itself around his and urged him on. *Come*, it said. *We have much to see.*

Tom was relieved to feel her presence. *Wait, I need to see more. I need to see the world he wants to create.* Soldiers raced across his vision, each figure short but powerfully built, their necks all but invisible and their faces broad with flat noses atop a wide slash of a mouth. Deep-set eyes sat beneath a heavy brow, and a single braid, interwoven with bones and other trophies hung low down their backs. They wore dark fatigues, tattered and patched in response to constant wear, and carried ugly looking weapons in large hands.

Their faces bore some resemblance to the face that had stared up at Tom as he had fought with Mr. Lampard, and he realised he was looking at the faces of An'Tsari soldiers. They were the troops Mr. Lampard would use to conquer and divide the people of a billion worlds if he were not stopped.

One soldier stepped forward, its roar like that of a wild animal. It stood amongst the ruins of a building, its arm beckoning its comrades to follow, and others raced to stand with it. Communication was limited to guttural sounds as they conversed, and as a single team they raced down a rubble-strewn incline and bulldozed their way into other buildings. Hapless figures struggled to escape, their race to avoid the rampaging soldiers futile. Screams were cut short by the staccato sound of weapons fire, and Tom cringed as bodies fell broken and bleeding in the half shadows.

The soldiers pounded on and Tom recoiled inside Mr. Lampard's mind. He pulled back from the horror of the scene, tears pricking his eyes, but knew he had to see more. As painful as the visions were, he had to follow their course until he knew precisely what Mr. Lampard intended to do.

Danny Forbes' voice tumbled into being, his words surfacing to remind Tom of the tortured visions he had witnessed.

'What I saw was a mistake. Somehow I was exposed to visions and knowledge that were not mine to see. Some people might say the visions I've seen are a privilege, an opportunity to reach out and touch the universe, but I wouldn't. After what they did to me, after what I've seen, I wouldn't wish them on anyone. I'd call them a curse.'

At that moment Tom understood what had terrified his father's friend so much. Without the mental capacity to grasp their full meaning, the visions Danny had seen would have been enough to break a normal human. They had almost done so, and tears filled Tom's eyes for the anguish the man had experienced, but he drew strength from the situation and delved once more into the visions before him.

He moved cautiously. The ruined cityscape unfolded before him, and everywhere he looked the forces pressed forward with their attack. Tom felt himself pulled deeper, and in each direction he found similar scenes of destruction and devastation. It was a torturous vision, and one he would not allow to happen.

This is what he wants to create, thought Tom. *This is the world we will have if he succeeds. He wants to seed as many planets as he can, and then return to them to conquer and rule.*

Tom blanched at the vision as soldiers took up firing positions above a group of figures. With an effort of will he drew away, the gruesome details lost within the scale of the scene, but froze as he recognised something in the landscape.

A great wheel-like structure stood high above the rooftops, its arcing form twisted by the devastating power of the attack on this world. Another change of viewpoint took him beyond its mangled form, dropping him low amongst rubble-strewn buildings until the true horror of the scene appeared, and he recognised where the destruction was taking place.

The burning ruins of the Houses of Parliament lay before him, their flames casting glowing reflections into the dark waters of the River Thames. Whitehall, its pale brickwork now blood-red as flames licked across its flanks, lay crumbled before him as swarms of soldiers flooded towards it across the devastated battleground. Beyond lay the remnants of Buckingham Palace, its mighty structure crumbled in the distance, burning like red eyes in the darkness.

Tom's mind was traumatised as he watched England's capital burn. Great warships hung low above the city, their destruction a wilful act of hatred as they split the darkness with their beams of crackling energy. He could do nothing but watch in distraught silence, the vision more than the dream of a tortured mind: it was a reality waiting to happen, a battle plan for the invasion which would come if Mr. Lampard were allowed to continue.

Tom knew he had to stop it, but how? He considered everything he had seen, everything the Gateway had offered, and knew there was only one way he could put an end to such lunatic dreams.

Pulling back, he broke contact with Mr. Lampard. His heart raced as the visions echoed inside his head like aftershocks, and he cast a trembling gaze at Annie. 'Can you keep him unconscious?' he asked. 'Can you keep him from interfering?'

Annie nodded and Tom stepped up to the controls. He stood before them for a moment, his fingertips hovering above the surface of the console, and then began to input symbols with steely determination. It seemed the direction his life had followed for so many years had now brought him to one final act.

It was an act that would decide everything.

CHAPTER 63

The universe shrunk to a tiny point of light.

Where are you taking us?

Annie's words flooded Tom's mind, the sensation pleasant and warming.

Somewhere safe, where he can do no harm, he replied. *He is as much a part of time and existence as you and I, but has no right to cause death and destruction purely for his own satisfaction. In the same way, I have no right to cause his death as a means of preventing his plan from succeeding.*

Annie understood the need to stop Mr. Lampard, and welcomed Tom's strength of character: it was a trait he had always displayed, and one to which she had been drawn. Now, she took strength from his presence once again.

Our people always believed in truth. We were a peaceful race, but there were those who strove to gain control and bring us to war, as on your world. Annie paused, and Tom sensed anguish in her thoughts. *I did not know he was one of them.*

Tom reflected on the images he had seen. *Did you resort to war, in the early days?*

Annie hesitated, her response jumbled as she considered what might have been. Finally, she composed herself.

Yes, but the global war that almost destroyed us was the final act which united us as a species. Without it, we would not have evolved to become who we are. Tom sensed discomfort in Annie's thoughts. *But on the eve of total destruction, at the very last moment, something happened, and we stepped back.*

What was it?

We called it 'The Awakening'. It was the moment when something changed within us. It was the first moment of our evolution, and from that point on all our energies turned outwards. We looked beyond our

218

own conflict, beyond our own world, and saw a universe worthy of exploration.

As in your own evolution, we grew from a more animalistic appearance and nature, but our evolution has been different. You started out much like us, but your genes have evolved, and your appearance is now very different.

Tom's thoughts were a great distance away. He remembered the Greys, the beings who had visited him as child, terrifying him and changing his whole perception of the future. Their great ship had hovered above his home, its penetrating lights slicing his world open, and leaving him to deal with the shattered truths of his childhood. *But your appearance is very different to the faces I witnessed earlier...*

Annie understood Tom's confusion. *You saw our earliest appearance, before we developed the technology to leave our home world and venture deep into the universe. Over time we evolved, and found we could take many forms. Ultimately, human form suited us best.* She indicated herself. *It was less frightening.* Annie's next words were chosen carefully, their effect calculated, and she spoke softly. *They would approve of what you are doing.*

Who would approve?

The Elders. Had they been here, I feel sure they would have approved of your course of action. Our species saw past the futility of war, and only by your actions has the one who wished to return us to those days been prevented from doing so.

Annie gazed up into the heavens as a universe expanded around them. A cluster of newborn stars wheeled above their heads, the surrounding clouds of nebulous gas lit from within to form glowing patterns. They passed through a Gateway, and the universe vanished in a flash of light.

They emerged amongst a veil of fresh stardust and soft light. Annie waited until the scene had expanded before she continued. *When the Elders were removed from power and banished from your universe, they believed the Gateway was secure. By not providing instructions on how to operate the device, they believed it would never be used again.*

Tom understood the implications of his own existence. *But they were unaware that the human race would evolve a mind capable of resurrecting the Gate.*

Annie smiled. *As I said, I believe they would have approved.*

This is the place. Tom indicated the giant super-galaxy they had seen as they first passed through the Gateway. It hung before him like a wondrous jewel, its light pure and beautiful: the light of creation. But now they had arrived, Tom felt apprehensive. He sensed a great loss burning within Annie, an emotion bubbling under the surface that masked her true emotions, and it troubled him.

This galaxy is newborn, thought Annie. *It is taking its first steps in the universe.*

A sense of wonder filled Tom as he studied it. The galaxy was a stunningly beautiful place, full of possibilities, and it seemed the most appropriate place to leave Mr. Lampard.

Tom knelt and peered intently at the old man. His features had softened as Annie held his consciousness, and he had returned to the image Tom had always known. He pondered the experiences they had shared together, and remembered the wonderful sights he had witnessed. *How much of it was true?* thought Tom. *How many of the visions I saw were real, and how many were merely the product of his tortured imagination?* Tom wanted to believe the visions of early Mars and of An'Tsa, and pursed his lips as he pondered their memory. He hoped he would have the opportunity to see many more such visions in his lifetime.

Annie placed her hand on Tom's shoulder, and he turned.

What do you intend to do?

Tom climbed slowly to his feet, but remained silent. He sensed Annie's discomfort, her weakened emotional state, but pressed on. It was something he had to do. It was more important than anything else.

I will leave him where he can observe new worlds evolving. He was there at the beginning of so many creations, so many galaxies, and it seems only right he should live out the rest of his existence where he can do the same. His consciousness can wander, and perhaps watching the birth of new worlds will temper his taste for destruction. Who knows, perhaps the life that he seeded there may thrive; it may evolve in its own time to become something he will appreciate.

Annie shrunk away, her back to Tom as she hugged herself. It was a human act; a gesture of self-control.

Tom watched, confused. *What is it? Do you think I'm wrong?*

Annie spoke aloud for the first time. 'No, you are right.' She turned and placed her arms around Tom's back and held him tightly as she spoke, her final words so soft that he almost missed them. 'Let me be with him.'

'Let you be with him? What, you mean stay here?' Tom broke their embrace. His body trembled at the thought of losing her once again, but her words were filled of tenderness and love, and he finally understood why.

'Tom, he's my father.'

CHAPTER 64

Annie's words stunned Tom into silence. He couldn't find the words to respond; couldn't voice any thoughts that would either accept or question her disclosure, yet somehow it all made sense.

She kissed him lightly on the forehead and smiled. Tom squeezed her hands. He nodded. 'Somehow, I've always known,' he said. 'I don't know how, but...' His voice faltered and he swallowed hard. Tears brimmed, but he fought them back. This wasn't the time – he'd lost Annie a long time ago, and this could never have been a rekindling of the love they had once shared. It had never been meant to be.

Annie kissed him again, and her mind reached out. Its presence was tender, and he felt his emotions begin to well up once more.

We are not that different, you and I. It was only time that prevented our existences from becoming one. Her words were filled with truth, and Tom understood the sentiment they carried.

Tom responded. *You said we were worlds apart. I suppose you were right.* He sighed as he smiled, his whole body sagging with emotion. *We were just not meant to be.*

Annie nodded, and a warmth passed between them; a fulfilling sense of love he had always treasured from their time together. He broke the moment with a question. *Where will you go first? What will you do together?*

Annie took her father by the hands and pulled him slowly to his feet. She turned his body inwards to face hers and wrapped an arm around tenderly around his back.

Watch.

A glittering tendril of purple-white light teased its way from Annie's head, her hair shining brightly in its reflected glare. The tendril worked its way around both bodies until they were encased within its glowing light.

We will exist in all times and all places. We will see everything, but will hinder nothing.

A thought struck Tom, and he sent it. *It seems your father will get his wish after all - you will be like gods.*

A purple tendril snaked outwards, its light moving gently, and a single word touched Tom's mind.

Come?

No. He stepped back and shook his head. *No.* The thought was quieter the second time, and he knew it was the right decision.

A warm feeling of gratitude flooded Tom's mind, and with that the light faded.

CHAPTER 65

The airlock cycled open and cold Martian atmosphere rushed in. Tom wondered what changes he would find outside, and was startled by a fine sheen of rain that glistened on the bare rock. He looked up as thick clouds rolled overhead. *So, this is it*, he thought. *The start of everything. Our very own Awakening.*

He stepped away from the airlock door and looked around. The sun was noticeably larger and brighter than Mars had known for billions of years, and Tom sensed the world had found a balance between its old orbit and the pull of the sun. If that were true, the rapidly thickening atmosphere and liquid water held deep within the planet would provide an opportunity for Mars' dormant life to thrive. The surface would soon become habitable, its air breathable, and a new world would emerge from the shadows of its tortured past.

We're taking our first steps in a larger universe, thought Tom. *We have two worlds to explore now; two worlds to nurture and two worlds on which to evolve.* He smiled, but thoughts of his missing friends stopped him cold. Without them here to share in the birth of this new world, every discovery would be tinged with sadness.

He remembered the last time they had all been together, the camaraderie that had filled their daily lives as they trained for the mission, and their absence hit him hard. His chest heaved as suppressed emotions surfaced, his true feelings exposed now the threat of Mr. Lampard had been lifted, and his breath came in great sobs. Dust filled his airways and he retched, his convulsions paralyzing him, and he could do nothing other than lie on the cold ground until they passed.

A whisper brushed his emotions aside and he raised his head to listen, unsure whether it was the sigh of the wind or merely his imagination, but the voice called to him again. This time a soft odour of summer flowers teased him, and he sensed the persona behind it.

He knew it was Annie.

Your friends are safe. Trust in me.

The words held greater meaning than anything Mr. Lampard had promised, and Tom was filled with hope. He called out, hoping Annie would respond, but the voice remained silent. Only the sound of dust could be heard as the light wind scattered it across the bedrock.

Was it possible they could still be alive? After everything they had been through, was it really possible?

Tom felt himself lifted by Annie's presence; it filled every part of him, flooded his soul with energy, and for a while he soared free of his body. His consciousness roamed across the landscape, and he traced his route towards the remains of *Foothold* station. It lay below him, its tangled remains scattered like litter across the cracked landscape.

As the new world passed beneath him he was drawn to a hill range peppered with boulders. In a cleft between the mountains a large circular pattern lay exposed. *The truth they hid will soon be revealed*, he thought. *Humanity will know its origins after all, and will have the opportunity to grow.*

He moved on, and a thin cloud of dust caught his attention. It crested a low hill and he raced passed it, skimming the surface until he returned at last to his own body. It lay in the dust, battered and scarred from its battle with Mr. Lampard, and he circled it once before becoming one with it again. His body jerked as if electrocuted, his first breath coming in a huge gasp, and he lay in the dust as his heart slowed.

Pushing himself into a sitting position he searched for Annie's presence. He felt warmed by the knowledge that somehow she had found a way to cross the boundaries of space and time, and knew he had not sensed the last of her.

The column of dust grew nearer and Tom climbed wearily to his feet. A vehicle slowed and came to rest a hundred metres before him, its bulk partially shielded by the dust that settled slowly in the low Martian gravity, but Tom recognised its design immediately.

A hatch swung open and a figure stood silhouetted against the light from within. It climbed down and moved purposefully forward, another figure close behind, and a familiar voice called out to him through the thin Martian atmosphere.

'Hey, buddy, how're you doin'?' Tiny's heavily bearded face was split by a huge grin. He stopped a few paces before his friend and laughed, but Naina raced past him and wrapped Tom in her arms. She hugged him tightly.

'I'm so glad you're safe, Tom. I really am.' She reached up and pulled his face towards her. 'But what happened? All those cuts and scrapes…?'

Tom hugged her back. 'Oh, you know me. If there's trouble, I'll find it.' He grinned and Tiny stepped forward and embraced his friend in a bear-hug.

'Aw man, it's so good to *see* you!' Tom winced as Tiny slapped him on the back, and the big man laughed again. 'What's up, man – feeling a bit sore?'

Tom pulled a face. 'Yeah, you could say that.' He changed the subject and the jovial reception quickly subsided. 'So, what's the situation? Have you heard anything from Riordan's crew?'

Naina's face dropped and Tiny's mood paled. He rubbed his fingers through his hair. 'Aw, mate, we haven't heard anything since we picked up their beacon, and that was over three weeks ago.' He grimaced. 'We've heard nothing since. I don't think Harriman had *any* intention of following through on his offer to look for them.' He sighed and shook his head. 'After you vanished we didn't see anybody.'

'But we'll keep looking,' added Naina. 'Until we know any different, we'll assume they're still alive. We owe them that.'

Tom smiled, his manner confident. 'They're alive.'

'How do you know?' Tiny was unconvinced. 'The chances of the whole crew surviving that…'

'Just trust me,' said Tom. 'Let's just say I have some inside information.'

'Inside information? What...how?'

Tom waved his hand, but didn't try to explain. 'It's quite a story,' he said. 'I'll fill you in on all the details later.'

Tiny snorted. 'Hey, after what we've seen these past few weeks, *nothing* will surprise me!' He grinned at Naina. 'Anyway, I think we might have a while to wait before we receive any help from home. You'll have plenty of time to explain.'

Tom indicated the vehicle. 'So, I take it this is ours now?'

Tiny nodded in agreement. 'It's as if they were never here,' he said. He shrugged. 'They just vanished.'

'They were here,' said Tom. 'Believe me, they were here.' He took his friends by the arms and stepped towards open hatchway. 'Come on,' he said. 'We've a lot to discuss.'

EPILOGUE

5 billion years in the future

A fleet of ships hung in formation around the swollen bulk of the sun. A vastly inflated red giant, it spread millions of kilometres out into space, but had long ago enveloped the orbits of the inner planets. Now, the two planets where life had first evolved lay scorched and barren.

The increase in the sun's size had not been a sudden event. The peoples of Earth and Mars had evacuated tens of thousands of years ago in preparation, but the event itself had been painful nonetheless. To see oceans and atmospheres boil away to space had caused great anguish, but the planets' final demise had been inevitable, and expected.

The inner planets of Mercury and Venus had long since vanished; their orbits engulfed by the sun as the star's ageing caused it to swell. Not that there had been much left for the sun to engulf: extensive mining had left the two inner planets as little more than hollow shells, their innards excavated for precious metals and minerals, while their surfaces had been left intact as protection for the miners who had dug away their valuable cores.

Even the gas giants of Jupiter and Saturn had not escaped the ravages of mankind. Hydrogen, helium and other valuable gases had been siphoned off to provide fuel for the colony ships that had left long ago. They now orbited the swollen star as shrunken shadows of their once majestic selves; their colours dulled, and Jupiter's Great Red Spot long since gone. Only the cold outer planets had been untouched by the fate of the sun, but recently they had become more hospitable, and for the last ten thousand years mankind had lived within the outer reaches of the solar system.

But that was about to end.

On this final day, the ships that hung around the sun did so in respectful silence as it burned through its final hours. They watched the twin planets where humankind had first evolved, and waited for the moment when they would be returned to the dust of space.

The humans who crewed the ships had not changed dramatically from the humans of long ago. Evolution had been kind; they had kept most of the qualities that made them human, but their intelligence had advanced greatly. They were now so far ahead of the first humans that the two were almost unrecognisable, yet they held great respect for their ancestors, and had assembled here to honour them in the last moments of their cradle's existence.

With a sudden flourish the sun increased its volume one final time. It crept ever nearer towards Earth and Mars, and its swollen bulk caused both worlds to crumble. It was the moment humanity had always known would come, and had been anticipated with dread.

The ships remained silent as a mark of respect towards their homeworld, but the silence was broken as they were commanded to edge closer to the swollen star. Despite the searing heat, beams of light snaked outwards between the ships, and they pulled together as one. As a single vessel they waited. The moment would come soon enough.

The Hub Ship was enclosed within the centre of the formation. Aboard it the Gate Master controlled the delicate manoeuvre they were about to undertake, but the time was not quite right, and he gave the command to hold.

The star exhausted its last gasps of fuel, but before it died it had one last duty to perform. As it collapsed into a white dwarf, the combined vessel shot forwards with blinding speed. It entered the star's remains and raced towards the converter the An'Tsari had planted there billions of years ago. Fully charged, the device released its stores of energy as the ship approached, and the star imploded.

From a safe distance it appeared as though the ship had been destroyed, crushed by the remains of the star as it fell in upon itself, but as the star was reduced to nothing, the space it had once occupied began to peel open like an expanding ring. Its edges pulsed with light and energy as the wormhole formed, and the great triangular ship hung at its centre like a shining jewel.

Across the ship's hull a single word was inscribed. It was a name written in great letters, passed down through the generations and uttered with reverence, and it shone with the reflected light of the stars. It was a name whose true meaning was understood by all.

HOPE.

The vessel hovered briefly, and with a pause to look back at the system that had created it, it slipped through the wormhole and vanished.

Also by
DAVID JOWSEY

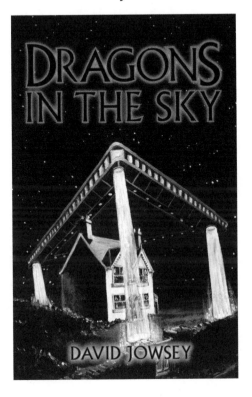

"Dragons in the Sky is an amazing adventure set against the most vivid backdrop of the moors. Atmospheric, frightening and yet most thrilling - a book that must be read."

GP Taylor, International best-selling author of Shadowmancer and The Curse of Salamander Street.

Available at your local bookseller or online at
www.sigelpress.com

The Countdown Begins...

SUMMER 2012

The spine-tingling conclusion to the
An'Tsari Trilogy.

Their shadows flickered in his dreams and their voices
whispered in the darkness.

They watched him until they were ready...
and then they came for him.

www.sigelpress.com